SECOND EDITION

Smartphones and Tablets Repairs:

Money Making Venture Skill

Chukky Oparandu

Picture Illustrations

Smartphones and Tablets Repairs:
Money Making Venture Skill

ISBN: 978-978-988-574-9

Mondraim Books®
A Subsidiary of Mondraim Nig. Ltd.

Printed in the USA by Amazon Kindle Direct Publishing

Available from Amazon.com, Barnes & Noble and other retail outlets
Also available on Kindle and other devices
For information regarding special discounts for bulk purchases,
Please contact mondraim@gmail.com or call +234-8035887084

Warning and Disclaimer

Dedication

To my darling Wife, Linda;

Chukwuma Jnr, Onyinyechi, Iheoma;

and my beloved mother, Joyce;

To these treasures God blessed me with, I dedicate this work.

Preface

Since the publication of the first edition of the book "*Mobile Phones and Tablets Repairs: A Complete Guide for Beginners and Professionals*" four years ago, a lot has happened in the mobile smartphone industry. But in spite of improvements and advancements in smartphone computing power, little has changed in terms of the underlying foundational technology. What has changed is a wider shift in user dependency rate than witnessed four years ago. Consumer behavior has experienced both attitudinal and trendy shift in more tremendous ways. The marginal utility value of a smartphone has astronomically risen despite rising cost of acquisition. Economists posit through the law of diminishing marginal utility that increasing consumption of goods leads to a decreasing price of the goods as marginal utility wanes. But smartphones have somehow managed to defy this law, making it one of life's highest valued assets.

According to a statistics published by **S. O'Dea**, Sep 2, 2020 on Statista website (https://www.statista.com) about Global smartphone sales to end users 2007-2021, "*in 2019, around 1.52 billion smartphones were sold worldwide. In the first quarter of 2020, around 86.3 percent of all **smartphones sold to end users** were phones with the Android operating system.*" He then adds, "*In 2019, the number of smartphones sold to consumers stood at around 1.52 billion units, a significant increase from the 680 million units sold in 2012. This means that over 19 percent of the world's total population owned a smart device in 2019, a figure that is expected to increase to **37 percent** by 2021. In 2018 smartphone penetration reached 60.5 percent in **North America. In the United States alone, sales of smartphones** were projected to be worth around 77.5 billion U.S. dollars in 2019, an increase from 18 billion dollars in 2010. By 2021, it is forecast that almost **84.3 percent of all mobile users** in the United States will own a smartphone, an increase from the 27 percent of mobile users in 2010.*" With the world's population today estimated at 7.8 billion, this is just the beginning.

Therefore, fixing Smartphones has become very much more lucrative an endeavor; a business with a very high return on investment. The Big opportunity lies in the fact that electronic gadgets are delicate devices which easily malfunctions when handled roughly. With a larger population of humans possessing either a smartphone or a tablet, the market potential for providing repair services and solutions is very promising. Aside the huge profit margin in selling personal skills, it opens doors for interfacing with a whole lot of people which could lead to greater business possibilities.

Tech Business serves as a catalyst for growth in all sectors of national economies. For example, besides food what else was of great importance during the covid-19 lockdown across the world?

Smartphones!

The first edition, "*Mobile Phones and Tablets Repairs: A Complete Guide for Beginners and Professionals*" covered in great length the subject of electronics in general and electronics' repairs from basic to fundamental principles and practical applications. It was an in-depth expository and I recommend it as a prequel to this second edition. This follow-up edition though also includes electronic circuit analysis, is designed to focus primarily on Smartphones and Tablets and its challenges with screen replacements as well as software.

Whereas there are both feature and minute technical design differences between basic or feature mobile phones and smartphone or tablets, fixing these devices require similar skillsets except in replacement of screens or display units.

Some critics or reviewers of the first edition kept asking, "Where are tablets? (Sic) (Referring to literal mention of Tablets)" while some were of the view that the knowledge and skills gained from the book satisfied their need as regards mobile phones technology and its repairs than for Tablets. But the beauty of the design of the former book, "*Mobile Phones and Tablets Repairs…*" lies in its coverage of the foundational knowledge inherent in the principles of electronics on which the technology of all mobile devices depends. The author considered the very fact that even as new Smartphones and Tablets would continue to be released into the market; those time-tested basic principles of electronics would always apply except for changes in software and compartmentalization of modules within the hardware.

Every technician who have been fortunate to train through the first edition is counted today among the best service technicians the world over...I repeat, the world over!

It bears repeating here, in conclusion that the best business is any venture organized towards meeting any one of mankind's most basic needs - it will always have a 'demand' market. This business venture remains a veritable self-reliance investment vehicle for anyone interested.

The author of this book has trained and empowered thousands of youths across many nations of the world. The result has been phenomenal. If there is any such time when the youths should be encouraged to look beyond the usual "Go to school, get a certificate, find a paid job" cycle, it is now.

Acknowledgments

I will always start by acknowledging the God of the universe who through the Holy Spirit inspired the writing and compilation of this work. The motivation could not have come from anywhere else other than the divine.

Among mortals came moral, intellectual and other forms of support. My family have been wonderful; my wife, my mum and kids.

Special thanks to all my members of staff and the editorial team. Your dedication, patience and labor of love is a great source of encouragement to me and very helpful in my pursuits.

I won't forget to thank my book cover designer and illustrator, Olamide Oladipo a.k.a Lammer, head of Creative at *Dudus Motive* and MD, *Activ8ed Prints*. From the first edition to my second book, *IT Career: A Roadmap* and this second edition, you are ever ready to make those zillions of changes with back and forth emails. Even as you are engrossed in your Master's program in Australia, at the peak of writing exams, you and your team still worked on my project. Thank you Lammer.

Thank you all.

Contents

PART 1

REVIEW OF BASIC KNOWLEDGE

&

TECHNICAL HARDWARE REPAIRS

This book is organized to teach any reader who follows through chapter after chapter as if he or she was attending a live training lab.

Chapter 1

Introduction to SMART Computing Technology

Communication is the process of exchanging data between two or more entities. It can be defined as "*the purposeful activity of information exchange between two or more participants in order to convey or receive the intended meanings through a shared system of signs and semiotic rules.*"[1]

In the telecommunication industry, a communication system refers to a collection of disparate communication networks, transmission systems, relay stations, tributary stations and data terminal equipment (DTE) usually capable of interconnection and interoperation to form an integrated whole.

The components of a communication system serve a common purpose, are technically compatible, use common procedures, respond to controls, and operate in union [1].

Communication systems are designed along with the implementation of specific data transmission and reception technologies. This means that the end device in the system (phones) must have the kind of radio access technologies that are compatible with the implemented technology within the communication system. The technology specification implemented by carrier companies determines the kind of radio access a smart phone or tablet phone uses to connect to the network, whether 3G, 4GLTE or 5G. Also, the RF (Radio Frequency) components in any given phone vary in both sophistication and complexity depending on the access technology standard they are designed to connect to.

In recent times, multiple-mode access phones are commonplace. Curiously, there exists no backward compatibility to older systems with the invention of newer technologies.

4G LTE

We have been in the age of 4ᵗʰ generation LTE (Long Term Evolution) technology, which is an advanced mobile cellular network standard in use today as the world is waiting to embrace the new 5G technology. Some countries have already tested and started the implementations for 5G.

4G LTE is not part of the ETSI (European Telecommunications Standard Institute) GSM standard. It is based on the GSM/EDGE and UMTS/HSPA network technologies, which increases the network capacity and speed using a different radio interface as well as core network improvements. It is a high-speed broadband standard for data and visual-centric information. Devices have data transmit speeds of 100mbps while in motion and 1Gbs when stationary.

Two main reasons 4G is faster than the erstwhile 3G are the implementation of Orthogonal Frequency-Division Multiplexing (OFDM) and Multiple-Input-Multiple-Output, or MIMO technique. OFDM is a technique for squeezing more data onto the same radio frequency spectrum thereby reducing latency (delay) and interference. Data is split up and sent through small blocks of frequency in parallel, therefore increasing the capacity of the network. MIMO is simply the use of multiple antenna arrays at both the transmitter and the receiver to improve communication performance.

5G

Like all other Gs, (G for generation) 5G is the fifth generation technology standard for broadband cellular or mobile networks. Since 2019, some cellular companies began deployment of this technology around the world as a replacement for the 4G LTE network.

In simple terms understand that major improvements in efficiency and speed, relative to the network signaling techniques used for transmitting radio frequency packets to and from wireless devices, are the key to change from one generation to another.

All cellular networks have a common, similar feature of breaking geographical areas being served into cells. Each 5g cell connects any 5G wireless device to both the internet and a telephone service via higher frequency radio waves propagated by a local antenna in the cell.

5G is expected to deliver higher bandwidth and speeds up to 10 Gigabits per second (GBit/s). Only 5G devices will be able to connect to 5G network infrastructure as there is no backward compatibility as usual. Also, due to the huge bandwidth radiated by 5G networks, the infrastructure will not only serve smartphones and tablets but would provide access to a whole range of computing and electronic devices such as laptops, desktops, and other devices leading to the internet of things. 5G networks may likely replace Internet Service Providers (ISPs) and cable companies.

The relationship between radio waves' length (wavelength) and frequency (the number of cycles per second of a wave) is an inverse one. Higher frequency waves have shorter wavelengths and vice versa. The 5G waves are referred to as millimeter waves, mmWaves. Therefore, the limited range of 5G waves is a trade-off for speed at mmWave frequencies.

What this means is that with the extremely higher frequencies of 5G networks, the waves will travel at shorter distances than the 4G, 3G and 2G waves. 5G towers will have shorter spaces between them per kilometer or mile. Some measurements have produced results of approximately 500 meters from a 5G tower. mmWaves are also susceptible to absorption by obstructions. With such short distances between cells and since the mmWaves cannot penetrate through obstructions, a higher density of radiation cell towers and antenna arrays propagating within neighborhoods becomes a given. Despite the massive benefits 5G will be bringing to consumers and businesses, there have also been concerns about public safety due to possible human exposure to high frequency radiation hazards.

Digital Smartphones and Tablets

Digital phones use the same radio technology as analog phones, but they use it differently. Analog systems hardly utilize fully the signal frequency spectrum between the phone (Mobile Station) and the cellular network due to the fact that analog signals do not undergo compression and signal manipulations as easily as pure digital signals.

Digital systems are much more efficient for signal transmission and reception. With digital systems more channels can be packed into a carrier company's allocated bandwidth which is an obvious advantage unlike with analog systems.

Digital phones convert the human voice (which is an analog signal) into binary information (1s and 0s) and then compress it before transmission. This compression allows between three to ten digital phone calls to utilize the same carrier frequency spectrum commensurate with a single analog call. Most digital cellular systems use frequency-shift keying (FSK) method for data transmission over legacy networks. FSK uses two frequencies, one for 1s and the other for 0s, alternating rapidly between the two to send digital information between the cell tower and the phone. Through the process of modulation and encoding, the analog information signal is converted to digital data, compressed and converted back to analog signal, retaining a high level of voice quality throughout the process. This is possible due to the strong processing power packed into digital cell phones.

Cellular Access Technologies

Access technologies refer to the method through which the user's message signals (voice, text, and data) gain access to the communication medium. Since in every cell there are multiple network users, "Multiple Access" denotes that in each access technology specification, more than one user is able to utilize the cell.

Three common technologies used by mobile cell phone networks for transmitting information are:

- Frequency Division Multiple Access (FDMA) which assigns a separate frequency for each call. FDMA separates the spectrum into distinct voice channels by splitting it into uniform blocks of bandwidth. This system is used mainly for analog transmissions. While it is capable of carrying digital information, FDMA is not that efficient for digital transmission.
- Time Division Multiple Access (TDMA) which assigns each call a fixed portion of time on a designated frequency. TDMA on the other hand has three times the capacity of an analog system using the same number of channels and operating in the 800-MHz (IS-54) or 1900-MHz (IS-136) frequency bands.
- Code Division Multiple Access (CDMA) which gives a unique code to each call and spreads it over the available frequencies.

However, the 4G and 5G network infrastructures use more enhanced, modified or advanced versions of these access technologies like the Orthogonal Frequency-Division Multiplexing (OFDM) combined with the Multiple-Input-Multiple-Output, or MIMO technique.

The Structural Design of Tablets and Smartphones

Form Factor

There used to be various physical designs of the legacy basic or feature mobile phones. But since production, the Tablet or Smartphone has retained one form or shape.

The form factor of a mobile phone refers to its size, shape and style, as well as the layout and position of its exterior physical aesthetics and parts. Having a good understanding of these sublime aspects of the design of a mobile device is important for a technician whose core job function primarily begins and ends with the task of disassembling and reassembling the phone to carry out corrective repairs. Three major form factors trended in the mobile phone market for years, mainly the bar phones (much like the tablet in smaller form), the flip phones, and the slider phones as well as subsets of these shapes. The "twist" design for instance was a subset of the flip type of mobile phones.

Figure 1.1a: Legacy bar phone

Tablets and smartphones have however retained the "bar" shape or form factor due primarily to the advancements in video/visual output of smartphones and tablets' multimedia functionality with integrated touchscreen input model. This was the game changer simultaneously with the development of Android and other Mobile Operating System software!

The "bar" or "tablet" form describes the shape of a rectangular bar or brick, but usually with rounded or curved corners or edges. This is the tablet or smartphone form factor that is dominant in the market today among all manufacturers and brands.

A common feature in the Bar-type tablet or smartphone is the full frontal wide-screen on the front face or fascia. Touchscreen phones, Tablet phones or the coinage "Phablet" (which means that they combine the functions of a smartphone and a tablet) phones are all subsets of the bar form. The very wide-screen size of Phablets and Tablets differentiate one from the other. They are usually larger than that of most touchscreen smartphones with most screen sizes measuring between 5.5 to 7.9 inches. You can hardly fit a Phablet phone comfortably into your pocket.

Figure 1.1b: Bar Smartphone

Smartphones

A smartphone combines the features of the traditional PDA and cellular phone, with a higher leaning towards the cellular phone functionality.

These hand-held devices integrate mobile phone capabilities with the more common features of a handheld computer or PDA. Smartphones allow users to store information, send and receive e-mails, and install programs alongside functioning as a mobile phone in one device.

There is no industry standard for what defines a smartphone, so any mobile device, which combines cellular and mobile computing functions, possesses more than basic feature phone capabilities with stronger hardware capabilities, and uses a mobile operating system can actually be rated under the smartphone category of devices.

Find listed below, Smartphones' historical milestones with respect to the two competing mobile operating systems (iOS vs. Android OS) till date:

☐ 1997– The term smartphone debuted

☐ 1999 - RIM began to make Blackberry phones

- ☐ 2007 - iPhone iOS 1.0 was released

- ☐ 2008 – iPhone iOS 2.0 and Android v1.0 were released

- ☐ 2009 – iPhone iOS 3.0 and Android 1.1 – 2.0 were released.

- ☐ 2010 – iPhone iOS 4.0 and Android 2.2 -2.3.7 were released

- ☐ 2011 – iPhone iOS 5.0 and Android 3.0 – 4.0.4 were released

- ☐ 2012 – iPhone iOS 6.0 and Android 4.1 – 4.3.1 released

- ☐ 2013 – iPhone iOS 7.0 and Android 4.4 – 4.4.4 released

- ☐ 2014 – iPhone iOS 8.0 and Android 5.0 – 5.1.1 released

- ☐ 2015 – iPhone iOS 9.0.1 and Android 6.0 – 6.0.1 released

- ☐ 2016 - iPhone iOS 9.3 – 10.0.1 and Android 7.0 – 7.1.2

- ☐ 2017 – iPhone iOS 11 and Android 8 - 8.1 were released

- ☐ 2018 – iPhone iOS 12 and Android 9 were released

- ☐ 2019 – iPhone iOS 13 and Android 10 were released

- ☐ 2020 – iPhone iOS 13.4 – 14.2 and Android 11 were released

Tablets

With the constant advancements in cellular access technology, device functionalities and capabilities also change. In the recent past, it was easier to differentiate a PDA from a smartphone simply by looking for touch-screen capabilities. If it had a touch screen it was a PDA, if it didn't, it was a smartphone. For example, Ericksson before it became Sony Ericsson made the first Smartphone, R380 which combined a touchscreen and a full QWERTY keyboard. The generic term for a PDA oriented device such as the Sony Ericsson phone described, having cellular phone capabilities is called a PDA phone.

Key Features of Smartphones and Tablets

The following are some features and capabilities which summarizes the functionalities built into smartphones and tablets which mobile cell phones do not have:

- Voice call
- Storage of contact information

- Make task or to-do lists
- Keep track of appointments and set reminders
- Use the built-in calculator for simple math
- Send or receive e-mail
- Get information (news, entertainment, stock quotes) from the internet
- Play games
- Watch TV
- Send SMS messages
- Integrate other devices such as PDAs, MP3 players
- Virtual Private Network (VPN)
- Near Field Communication
- Wi-Fi Connectivity
- Bluetooth
- GPS
- Camera/ Video capabilities
- Internet Communication sharing (Hotspot)
- Third-party applications support

Chapter 2

Components Identification and Features

Smartphones are just like PCs in their hardware component make-up. Like a PC they have a processor, input and output devices, power management, and radio (cellular) etcetera. The modern smartphone is basically a micro-computer. Unlike a PC that has PCI slots, SATA controllers and ports, memory slots and so on, smartphones have these equivalents but hard-soldered directly to the circuit board.

Tablets and smartphones just like the old mobile phones retain these extension peripherals embedded on their motherboards which serve to aid the functionality of the main board or motherboard. Without these peripherals attached at various interfaces, the device would not function as purposed.

In the first edition, "Mobile Phone and Tablets Repairs..." these components and their differences were examined in details. We shall do a quick look at some of the structural differences or similarities with 'basic' or 'feature' mobile phones in this edition.

Just a reminder, since the objective of this book is to teach you to be able to fix any model of tablet or smartphone that comes your way, it is important that each item found on the motherboard of the phone is properly identified, its function understood, its specific location on the motherboard identified and above all its functional or failure status determined by the technician. The motherboard is designed to maximize circuit board real estate while minimizing cost. A smartphone motherboard is usually organized to conform to a specific form factor, dictated by the manufacturing company. The size and space constraints and costs make the tablet or smartphone's design less generic.

Today's smartphones utilize what is referred to as System on Chip or SOC technology whereby the processor and other vital ICs (Integrated Circuit) integrate several functions into a single chip.

Finally, note that spare parts found in tablets or smartphones regardless of the manufacturer's brand; whether Apple, HTC, SonyEricsson, Samsung, LG, Huawei, Chinese brands and so on, differ only in their style of internal fixture, shapes, sizes or other form factor. Apart from these, their major functions remain the same across models.

Peripheral Input/ Output Units

This refers to components that are attached as auxiliaries to the motherboard of the device besides the external casing of the phone. The following are considered as peripherals;

Batteries

The battery is the primary source of power to the mobile phone. It supplies optimum D.C (Direct Current) voltage of between 3.6v to 3.8v and is shut down by the phone at below 3.1v D.C.

Most mobile phone designs provide for a user-removable back cover to gain access to the battery. But today, we have a predominance of non-removable battery designs, whereby the batteries are sealed within the casing of the phone and can only be accessed by a technician when the phone is disassembled altogether.

Battery Connectors

The battery connector provides interface between the phone's motherboard and the battery. Tablets and most smartphones have advanced from the copper pin-type connectors shown below used in basic and feature phones to flex connectors while still retaining the pin (cord) configurations, some two while others are four pins (or cords).

Figure 2.1: Legacy Battery Connectors

The first and last pins are usually the positive and negative terminals respectively while the middle pin(s) comprises of the battery status indicator (BSI) pin, sometimes including the battery temperature sensor pin, BTemp.

Figure 2.2: Smartphone or Tablet's Batteries

Microphones

The microphone or Mic for short usually called 'mouth-piece' in the mobile repair industry is a device that converts sound waves (human voice signal) into electrical signal in the phone which is then transmitted to the receiver station.

Microphones are usually located towards the base of the phone relative to the placement of the phone between the ear (top) and the mouth (base or bottom) during a phone call. Below are some sample images of varieties of legacy phones' and smartphones or tablets' microphones in fig.2.3a and fig. 2.3b;

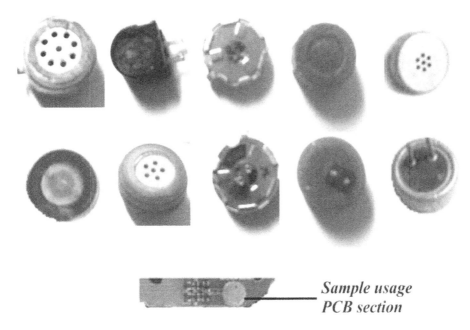

Figure 2.3a: Legacy Microphones (mouthpieces)

Figure 2.3b: Smartphones' Microphones (mouthpieces)

Speakers

The speaker is also called the 'ear-piece'. It provides the user of the handset with audio output from the caller.

This device is placed at the anterior (head) part of the phone relative to the position of the ear during a phone call. See sample images for both legacy phones and smartphone or tablets speakers in fig. 2.4a and fig. 2.4b respectively;

Speakers

Figure 2.4: Legacy Phones' Speakers

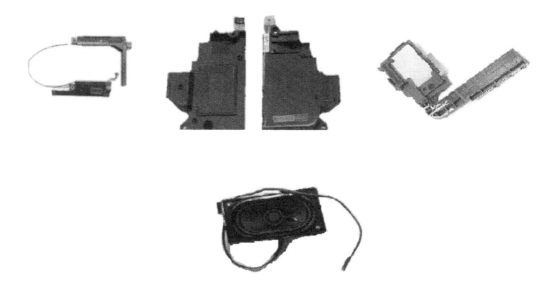

Figure 2.4b: Smartphones and Tablets' Speakers

Ringers

Ringers provide both multimedia audio output and caller alert to users for incoming calls to the mobile device. Some ringers actually appear similar in shape and form with speakers and some too have dual functions as speakers and ringers combined, or speaker/ringer/vibrator all in one unit.

iPhone Ringer/Speaker

You will find more samples of ringers in Figure 2.5.

Vibrators

Vibrators also provide users with alert but in a silent manner by causing the vibration of the phone. They are made up of a D.C motor which is electromechanical in nature as electrical signal causes the rotation of the rotor within an armature.

Find sample images of various vibrator types below. With the compiled images in fig. 2.6, you cannot go wrong in identifying what component is a vibrator within a mobile phone assembly.

Figure 2.5: Ringers

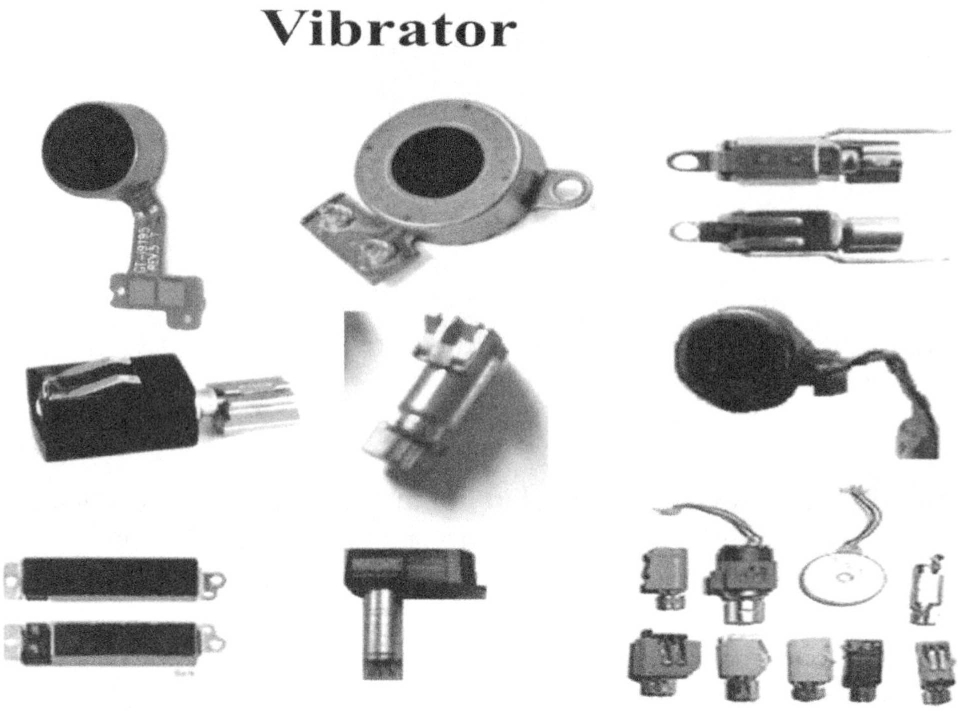

Vibrator

Figure 2.6: Vibrators

Charging Ports

Charging ports are the connecting points for mobile phone chargers to transfer recharge voltage to the battery through the charging circuitry of the motherboard. They come in either pin-type design or modular USB data interface ports type. Find images of sample charging ports in fig. 2.7 below.

Figure 2.7a: Legacy Charging Ports

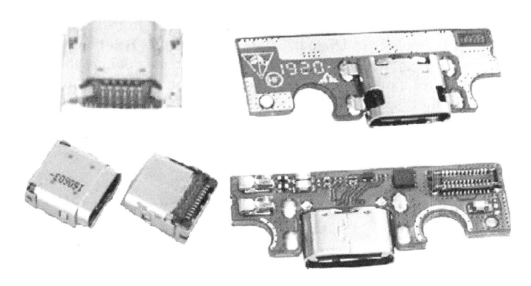

Figure 2.7b: Smartphones USB-C Charging Ports

Display Units of Tablets and Smartphones

Display units are field replaceable units. One doesn't need to fix them if they are damaged. Just swap with a new one. Simple!

Although in my lab, I have attempted several times to fix them and made huge dollars out of doing that, because I understand how they work if not broken. If broken there is nothing you can do about that. But I must caution; be sincere with your client. Never say you are changing screen, then succeed in fixing it and take money for a new one. That's plain dishonest. State what you would do, charge what you wish, and earn it sincerely.

This book and the subject of Tablets or Smartphones' repairs would be devoted mostly to screen replacement tasks and software issues. In this age of large screens and sealed devices, majority of repair operations (even as minor as replacing a battery) and its success depends very much on the ability to remove and replace the screen. Otherwise, no one can gain access to any of the internal parts of the device for repairs.

The display unit is the phone's visual or video output system for user interface. Tablets and smartphones are equipped with capacitive touch sensing technology screens for user keyboard input. Usually the main screen is the Liquid Crystal Display (LCD) overlaid with more recent touch sensing technology screens or glass called the digitizer.

In some instances, both the LCD and digitizer are fused together while in others, the glass digitizer is overlaid on the main screen for touch sensing input and connected separately with its own flexible cable.

There are various screen technologies in the market ranging from TFT (Thin-Film-Transistor technology LCD), to IDS (Interactive Display Solutions) or AMOLED. Samsung created the Super AMOLED which incorporates the capacitive touchscreen, rather than as a separate layer on top of the display unit. This makes the display unit or screen thinner.

Screens

Figure 2.8: Legacy LCD Screens

Figure 2.8b: Digitizer (L) and LCD Screen (R)

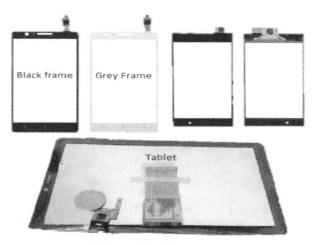

Figure 2.8c: Digitizers

Figure 2.8d: Back View of Smartphones' LCDs

Some screens are sold complete with the frame as seen in the figure below;

Figure 2.8e: front and Back View of Smartphones' LCDs

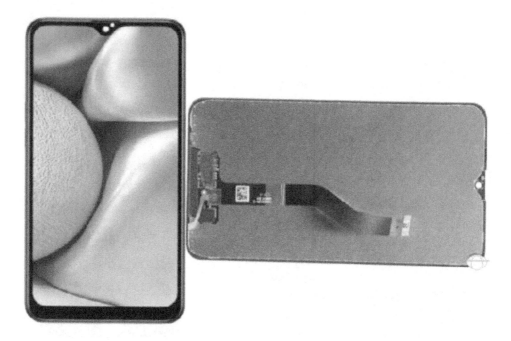

Figure 2.8f: Front and Back View of Smartphones'

Notice the long ribbon cable (R) at the back of the screen in fig 2.8f. When dealing with screen removal which would still be reused, extreme care must be applied to avoid any slight cut or abrasion on the flexible cables. Note that the only difference with Tablets' screens is in the larger size of the screen.

Each screen technology deployed has its pros and cons, although as a technician your job is to successfully replace a bad screen with a similarly good one for any model.

But in terms of characteristics, TFT for instance has a lower energy consumption especially when dealing with bigger Tablet screens. That in itself is an advantage. TFT displays are very sharp and also very attractive. There are also variants of TFT like the TN-TFT (Twisted Nematic-TFT) and the recent PLS-TFT (Plane Line Switching TFT technology) developed by Samsung which competes with IPS (In Plane Switching) screen technology. It has better image quality compared to TN-TFT and equals IPS. They have near accurate color reproduction, great viewing angles and are the best when it comes to outdoor legibility due to their higher brightness levels. Although with such brightness levels, energy consumption is higher.

AMOLED is an acronym which stands for Active Matrix Organic Light Emitting Diode. There is also the Passive Matrix OLED. It is just a terminology describing the technology used to power the luminescent property of screens when projected on the liquid crystals. In this case, organic compounds form the electro-luminescent material while active matrix is the technology used to address the pixels.

Simply stated, it means that when electric current is passed through these organic compounds, they emit light.

Display Connectors

Connectors provide connection points where the LCD screens are attached to the motherboard. There are various types. For some, the screen is attached to the interface point through a flexible connector. This is now mostly used in latest smartphones and Tablets.

   Also note that flexible connectors are not only used for connecting LCDs but also camera, keypad, volume keys, etc.

Figure 2.9a: Legacy LCD Connectors

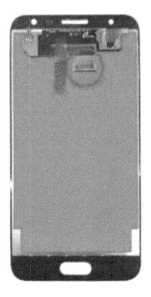

Figure 2.9b: Current LCD Connectors

ON-OFF and Side Button Switches

Switches are used in various forms for various functions in the mobile phone. There are physical on/off push button switches for power-on functions, side volume up/down switches, camera buttons etc. In other cases they are logical buttons that trigger a logic "1"/ "0" pulse.

Below are sample shots of physical switches soldered to the motherboard of phones, but usually enclosed in beautiful, sleek rubber or plastic buttons on the outside.

See sample switch images in fig. 2.10;

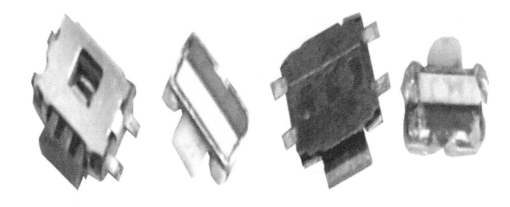

Figure 2.10a: Legacy Push-button Switches

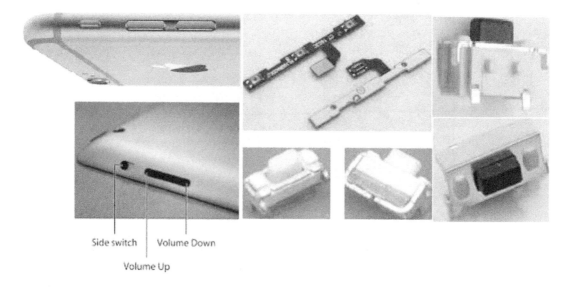

Side switch | Volume Down

Volume Up

Figure 2.10b: Current Push-button Micro-Switches

SIM Card Connector/Tray

SIM (Subscriber Identity Module) connector provides interface between the SIM card and the motherboard of the phone.

The SIM card itself is a smart memory chip supplied to the user by the chosen telecommunication carrier which contains information about that particular user, identifies him/her as a legitimate subscriber and provides access to network services.

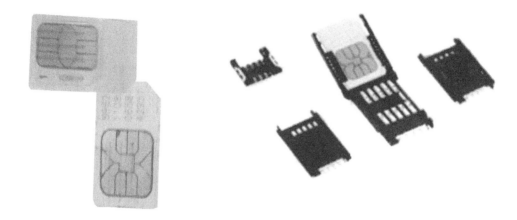

Figure 2.12a: Full SIM Card and SIM Connectors

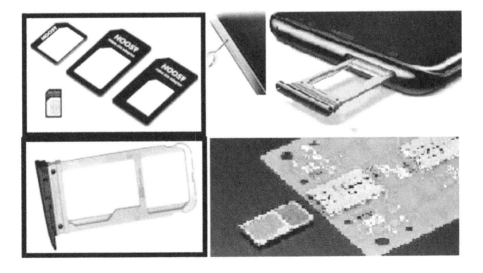

Figure 2.12: Micro SIM Card Adapters and Connectors

Memory Card Connectors

Memory cards which provide external or extended storage capacity for the mobile phone user are interfaced to the mobile device through the memory card connector embedded on the motherboard;

Figure 2.13: Memory Card Connectors

Camera Module

Tablets and smartphones are equipped with various calibers of camera for taking pictures. They are connected to the motherboard through interface socket points.

Camera On-Board Connector

Camera

Figure 2.14: Camera modules and Connectors

Headphone Jack/Connector

This provides point of connection for external earphones or 'hands-free' cord earphones.

Figure 2.15: Mobile Phone Hands-free Ports

Antenna

The antenna couples inbound and outbound message signals to and from the mobile device. This means that the antenna functions primarily to transmit and receive signals.

The older mobile phones had their antennas sticking out from the body of the phone. Nowadays most antennas are inbuilt and only accessible when the phone is disassembled.

There are various ways and forms antennas are built into the motherboard. A technician must observe to identify these representations. Example pictures below are some samples for old and new models.

Antennas

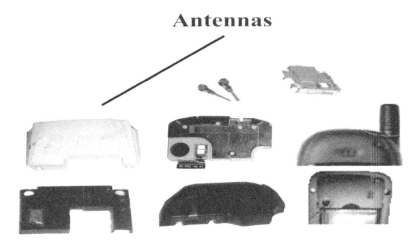

Figure 2.16: Legacy Antenna System Components

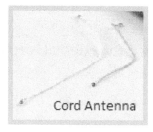

Figure 2.16: Cord Antenna Currently Used in Smartphones and Tablets

Electronic Motherboard Components

Internal electronic components for bigger electronics devices or digital devices naturally consist of bigger chip packages compared to the microelectronic components found in smartphones and tablets. Snapshots of both the bigger components and their equivalent microelectronic forms as found in the smartphones and tablets are shown below.

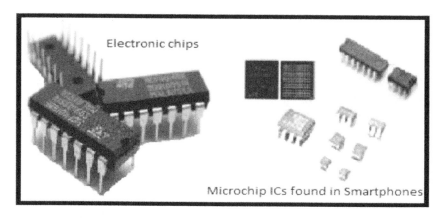

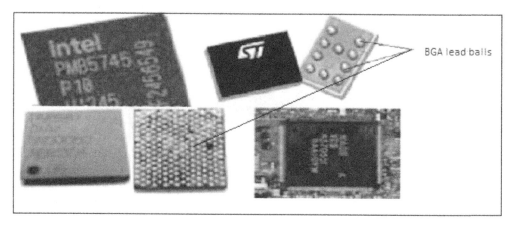

Figure 2.17 Various Types and Sizes of Integrated Circuit Packages (ICs)

Transistors

Emitter

Base

Collector

Transistor as Seen in Phones =>

Figure 2.18: Transistors

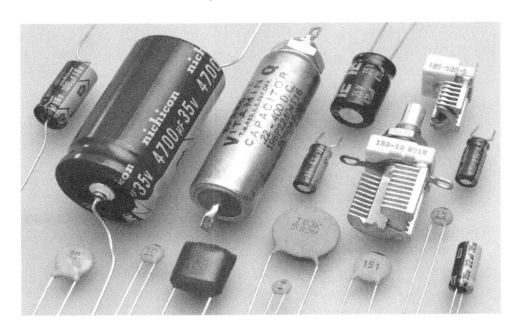

The picture above shows bigger electronic components found in household electronics. Capacitors used in microelectronics are in smaller form factors and with specific colors.

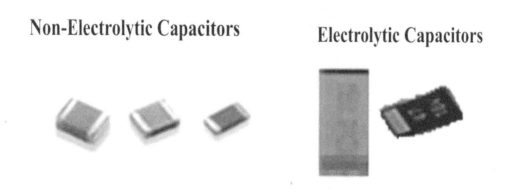

Figure 2.19: Capacitors

Diodes

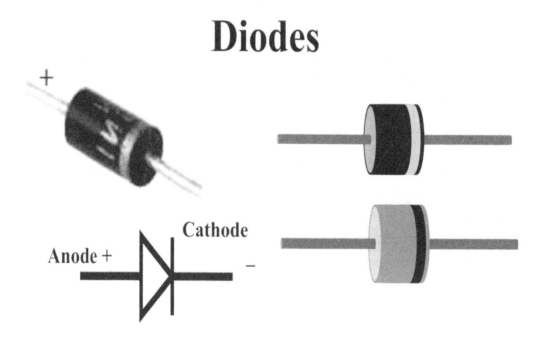

Diodes found in smartphones and tablets phones are also smaller in size;

PCB Diodes

Figure 2.20: Diodes

INDUCTORS

In a smartphone or tablet you would find tinier inductors as shown below;

Figure 2.21: An Inductor

Resistor

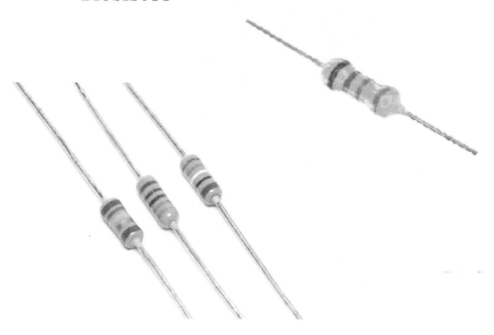

On smartphone PCBs, you will find resistors in smaller forms as shown below;

Figure 2.22: Resistors

All the internal electronic components above are found in smaller form factors in the mobile phone as seen in the image clip below;

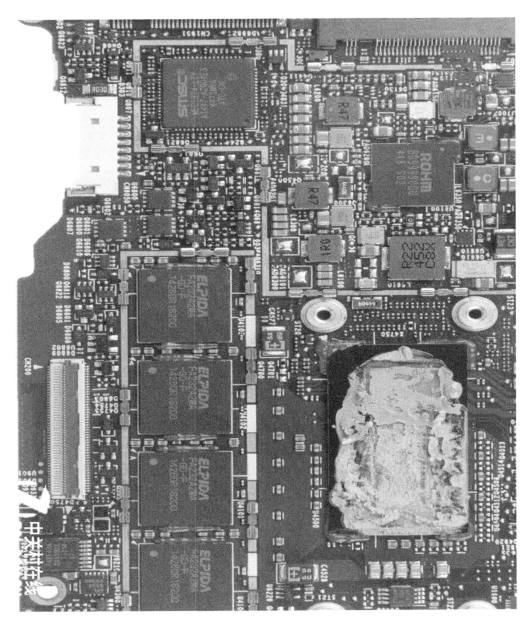

Figure 2.23: Sample cross-section of internal electronic board

In order to differentiate these components appropriately and diagnose faults, it is important for a technician to acquire in-depth knowledge of meter reading process and circuit analysis to carry out electrical level troubleshooting and repairs.

Chapter 3

Basic Electronics and Circuits Analysis

The field of electronics gave birth to most of the technological products being enjoyed by mankind today. Computers for instance, owe their existence to the field of electronics. Electronics technology has its roots in the discovery of electricity; that branch of science that deals with electrical phenomena, discovered through the application of the principles of physics.

This chapter is very important for technicians in order to understand the foundational basis upon which they can be proficient in their craft. The reason is simple. When you understand electronic components; their names, their functions and behavior in the circuit, how they fail, how to test and verify their status (functional or non-functional) and how they are interconnected with each other, then your task is easy. This is my objective in teaching this basic electronics foundational course.

Although there are variety of manufacturers or brands of smartphones or tablets, and within each brand there are also several models; however, beneath the casings of these diverse products are the same electronic parts. Parts manufacturers do not care about brands. While certain custom made specifications and quality ratings may differ across brand names, the parts are mostly similar, and the same parts' manufacturers actually supplies two or more competing phone brands. For instance, the processors found in phones are made by chip manufacturers like Intel, Skyworks, Qualcomm, MediaTek, SpreadTrum, Broadcom, Coolsand etc. The ICs or other chipsets made by these manufacturers can be used by Samsung, Nokia (Microsoft), Infinix, Tecno, LG, Xiaomi etc.

The same applies to peripheral components like speakers, microphones, ringer etcetera. Based on their form factors and allocated PCB space, two unrelated brands of mobile device can interchange parts with similar form factors during repairs. A Samsung microphone of the same size as an LG microphone can be used during a repair or replacement job. What this means is that, at face value, customers buy brand names.

Consequently, understanding the properties of the mainboard's electronic components is important. Let me start by inculcating perspectives in your thought process using existing simple definitions which explains the organization or structure of knowledge. In my book, *IT Career: A Roadmap*, I expounded on the essence and the inter-relationships between the various foundational disciplines and ICT, IT career roles and guides to earning a spot in the IT industry.

Definitions

Physics is that branch of science concerned with the study of properties and interactions of space, time, matter and energy. At secondary or high school class, you might have undertaken this subject.

Electricity is the branch of science that deals with *electrical* phenomena which is the set of physical occurrences related to the presence and flow of electric charge.

Electrical **engineering** is a branch of engineering that deals with the *technology* of electricity, especially the design and application of circuitry and equipment for power generation and distribution, machine control and communications.

Technology, on the other hand is the study of or a collection of techniques.

In conclusion, *Electronics* is the study and *use* of *electrical devices* that operate by controlling the flow of electrons or other electrically charged particles. Electronics deals with the technology of utilization of electricity.

After the discovery of electricity, electrical power, its generation and distribution capacity, the question one needed to ask was, "to what use?" How will mankind benefit from this energy flowing across conductors? In every home, office and wherever man is found today, aside the incandescent bulb invented by the great Thomas Edison, there is no other use for electricity except for electronic devices and products which are powered by electrical energy.

In this chapter, we shall discuss basic electronic theories and practices needed as a foundation for the task of becoming a field electronic technician in the specialized area of microelectronics.

Principles and Concepts of Electricity

Centuries ago, a number of scientists became interested in the observation of some natural phenomenon about the electric charge. Some particular substances were observed to exhibit the tendency to attract when brought close to each other. For some substances, this was observed after being rubbed together. This observation became known as static electricity.

The Genesis of Electrical Polarity (Positive and Negative)

It started with Benjamin Franklin's observation that silk and glass would tend to stick together when a glass rod is rubbed on silk for a period of time. An observable attraction force seems to be pulling both materials towards each other, demonstrated once attempt is made to separate the two materials. Other materials that behaved in a similar manner were a pair of wax and wool. However, further investigation of this phenomenon exposed the fact that the invincible force of attraction between these two substances after being rubbed together also acted in opposite direction when like objects were placed together, resulting in the conclusion that there exists two forces;

- Attraction Force and
- Repulsion Force

Furthermore, it was postulated from the fact of observation of these materials that;

Like objects repel each other while *unlike objects attract each other*.

One of the hypothetical conclusions drawn from the scientific observation of these objects and their behavior when rubbed together was that more than one kind of change occurred whenever these materials were rubbed together;

- That invisible "fluids" known as "charges" were being transferred from one object to another during the rubbing process and
- That these fluids had the capacity to exert a physical force over a distance.

Benjamin Franklin later came up with the conclusion that there was only one "fluid" exchange taking place between rubbed objects and that the two different "charges" of the fluids were nothing more than either an **excess** or a **deficiency** of that one fluid!

After further experiments, following Benjamin Franklin's speculation of the wool rubbing off of the wax, the type of charge associated with 'rubbed' wax became known as "negative" (due to <u>assumed</u> deficiency of fluid) while that associated with 'rubbing' wool became known as "positive" (due to its <u>assumed</u> gain of excess fluid). Later discoveries exposed the fact that the "fluid" comprised of extremely small bits of matter called *Electrons.*

These extended experiments revealed that all objects are made up of extremely small building blocks known as "Atoms". Atoms are in turn composed of particles which further comprise of three smaller fundamental particles known as *Protons, Neutrons* and *Electrons.*

The branch of natural science that deals with the composition and constitution of substances and the changes that they undergo as a consequence of their molecules is known as Chemistry. Any reader who would like to delve further into this study is free to do so since, for the purposes of this book, we will go no further than the basics required for technical proficiency. Our focus here is on the behavior and properties of the electrons which is a subatomic component of matter.

Protons and the neutrons are contained in the nucleus of an atom. The tightly knit combination of neutrons and protons in an atom provides stability and differs from the spaced out electrons that are more mobile and orbiting around the nucleus of an atom. So even though each atom in a piece of material tends to hold together as a unit, there is actually a whole lot of empty space between the orbiting electrons and the cluster of protons and neutrons in the center of the atom. Electrons are so free to move about that they can even be knocked out of their respective positions in the atom or entirely out of the atom by very negligible energy compared to what is required to knock out particles in the nucleus.

Whenever this happens, although the atom retains its chemical identity, an imbalance occurs. There is a force of attraction between the orbital electrons and the protons in the nucleus of an atom. It is this attraction force that makes it possible for electrons in the atom of an object to travel a distance to reside around atoms of another object.

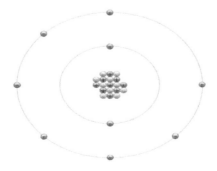

Figure 3.1: Atomic Structure
Credit: Wikimedia

Electrons and protons are of opposite polarity to each other; hence, are attracted to each other in an atom. Protons however are held bound in the nucleus of an atom due to another force called Nuclear force.

In every atom, there are equal and opposite number of these particles such that their attraction and repulsion forces cancel out. Remember that like charges repel while unlike charges attract each other. Each electron has a negative charge, while each proton has a positive charge. Being of equal numbers within an atom, they counteract each other's presence so that the net charge within the atom is zero. If electrons leave or extra electrons arrive, the atom's net electric charge will be imbalanced, leaving the atom "charged" as a whole, causing it to interact with charged particles and other charged atoms nearby.

Neutrons are electrically neutral as they do not attract or repel electrons or protons or even similar neutrons. They have no charge altogether. The effect of rubbing together two distinct materials of specific qualities is that electrons are either absorbed or discharged from one material to the other; electrons from the atoms of one material are forced by the rubbing action to leave their respective atoms and transfer to the atoms of the other material. In other words, electrons are made up of the "fluid" hypothesized by Benjamin Franklin. The result of an imbalance in this "fluid" (electrons) between objects is called "static" electricity because the displaced electrons tend to remain static after being moved from one insulating material to another.

In the case of rubbing wax and wool together, further experimentation revealed that electrons in the wool actually transferred to the atoms in the wax, which is exactly contrary to Benjamin Franklin's hypothesis! But in his honor for designating the wax's charge as being "negative" and the wool's charge as "positive," electrons are said to have a "negative" charge. *Thus, any object whose atoms received an excess of electrons is said to be negatively charged, while an object whose atoms are deficient of electrons is said to be positively charged.*

In 1832, Michael Faraday proved that static electricity was the same as the electricity produced by a battery or a generator. On PCBs for instance, static electricity is capable of causing damage to sensitive semiconductor circuitry, the reason technicians are required to wear anti-static wrist straps.

Consequently, an electric current is defined as a flow of electric charge. In electric circuits this charge is often carried by moving electrons in a wire. It can also be carried by ions in an electrolyte, or by both ions and electrons. Electrical current flows through an electrical conductor from one end to the other. It was these principles and concepts of electricity that gave rise to electrical quantities in electrical circuits such as Current, Voltage, Resistance, Power etc.

Whenever a conductive path is created to allow free electrons to continuously move in order to achieve a specific purpose, an electric circuit is formed. This continuous movement of free electrons through the conductors of a circuit is what is referred to as current, and it is often referenced in terms of "flow," just like the flow of a liquid through a hollow pipe. However, in order to motivate these electrons to "flow" in a circuit, there is what is known as electromotive force called voltage or e.m.f.

Voltage is a measure of the potential energy <u>relative</u> to two points in a circuit. The presence of voltage at any point in a circuit is a measure of the amount of potential energy available to move electrons from one reference point (A) in that circuit to another reference point (B). The free electrons in the orbit of atoms tend to move through conductors with a certain level of friction or opposition to motion. This opposition to motion is called resistance.

The Difference between Convention Current and Electron Flow

Benjamin Franklin's statement regarding the direction of flow of charge (from the wax to the wool instead of wool to wax), became a determinant for the use of the electrical notation of current flowing from positive to negative direction despite the fact that it is clear that electrons are the constituent units of charge, and that they are displaced from the wool to the wax — not from the wax to the wool — when the two substances are rubbed together. This is why electrons are said to have a negative charge, because Benjamin Franklin assumed *in error* that electric charge moved in the opposite direction than it actually does, therefore what he called "negative" (representing a deficiency of charge) in reality was an excess of electrons. Eventually, when the true direction of electron flow was discovered, the notation of "positive" and "negative" had become well-grounded among scientists. It became accepted and therefore became known as *conventional flow or current.* But if charge flow is designated according to the actual direction of movement of electrons in a circuit, it is known as *electron flow notation.*

In conventional flow notation, we show the motion of charge according to the labels of (+) and (-) although this, technically speaking, is not the true direction of motion. This way, the labels make sense but the actual direction of charge flow is incorrect. In electron flow notation, we follow the actual direction of motion of electrons in the circuit, but the (+) and (-) labels are in the reverse.

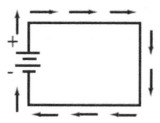

Figure 3.2a: Conventional flow from positive to negative terminal

Figure 3.2b: Electron flow from negative to positive terminal

Any notation chosen will lead to equal success as you analyze circuits, either as an imaginary conventional flow of current or the real electron flow direction.

Conductors and Insulators

The electrons of various kinds of atoms have different degrees of freedom to move around which depends mainly on the types of materials they are comprised of. Metals for instance have their outermost electrons loosely bound to their atoms such that they move freely in the space between the atoms of their material, making it easy for them to be dislodged by the influence of heat energy (See figure 6.1 again). Because these loose electrons are free to leave their respective atoms and move around in the space between adjacent atoms, they are called free electrons.

But for materials like rubber or glass, the electrons in their atoms have very little freedom for motion. While external forces such as heat energy or physical rubbing can force some of these electrons to leave their respective atoms and transfer to the atoms of other materials, they do not move between atoms within rubber or glass materials very easily like metals. This ability of electrons to move about within a material is a quality known as electrical conductivity.

The Conductivity of a material is determined by the types of atoms in such materials (the number of protons in each atom's nucleus, which determines its chemical identity) and how the atoms are linked together with one another. Materials with large free electrons are called **conductors**, while materials with small or no free electrons are called **insulators.** Examples of conductors include silver, copper, gold, aluminum, iron and steel while insulators include materials like plastic, wood, rubber, leader etc.

Just as there are differences between conductors and insulators, different materials also have varying degrees of either conductivity or insulation property. Whereas the normal motion of "free" electrons in a conductor is random, with no particular direction or speed, electrons can be influenced to move in a uniform manner through a conductive material. This uniform motion of electrons is what we call *electricity*, or *electric current*. Just as water flows through hollow pipes to supply water from a tank, so also electrons flow through the hollow of conductors around an electrical or electronic circuit.

Electrical Continuity

For a strip of conductive metal to allow electron flow in a continuous manner end- to-end, there must be a source and a destination.

A continuous piece of conductor

To get electrons to flow through this conductor or piece of wire, we have to add a source and a destination.

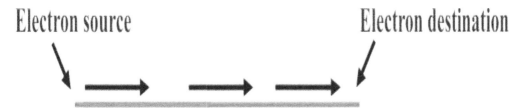

With the Electron Source pushing new electrons into the wire on the left-hand side, electron- flow through the wire can occur (as indicated by the arrows pointing from left to right). However, this flow of electrons will be interrupted if the conductive path formed by the wire is broken at any point as shown in the image below;

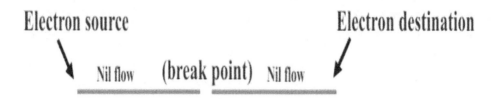

Once there is a break in the conductor, electron flow stops at the edge. The solution to situations of this nature is to create a jump wire across the break point. This is what technicians do to correct such faults in electrical circuits. See the image below;

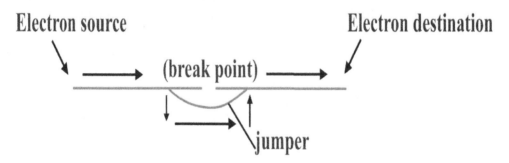

The "jumper" when introduced, re-routes the electron flow around the break point, creating a continuous path towards the destination.

Conductors do have negligible intrinsic resistance present in their constituent materials due to frictional resistance encountered by moving electrons, as is often said, "There is no perfect electrical conductor". Perfect electrical conductors only exist in the ideal sense, used in situations where there is zero resistivity (impossible in reality). This resistance is what causes the warmth or increase in temperature of conductors in any working electrical circuit.

Electrical Quantities and their Relationships

As a prelude to exploring the world of electricity and electronics, it is vital to start by understanding the three basic electrical quantities which are the three basic building blocks required to manipulate and utilize electricity namely voltage, current and resistance. In any circuit, the amount of current flowing depends on the amount of voltage available to motivate the electrons, and also the amount of resistance in the circuit to oppose electron flow. Just like voltage, resistance is a quantity relative to two points.

Units of Measurement

Voltage (V): The unit of measurement of Voltage, symbolized by the alphabet "V" is Volt in honor of the Italian physicist Alessandro Volta (1745–1827), who invented the voltaic pile, possibly the first chemical battery. One volt (1V) is defined as the difference in electric potential between two points of a conducting wire when an

Electric current of one ampere (1A) dissipates one watt (1W) of power between those two points.

Current: The unit of measurement of current, symbolized by the alphabet "I" is Ampere, named after André-Marie Ampère (1775–1836), French mathematician and physicist, considered the father of electrodynamics. The ampere is a unit of current, which is the amount of charge transiting per unit time, while the coulomb is a unit of charge. The ampere is defined as the constant current that will produce an attractive force of 2×10^{-7} Newtons per metre of length between two straight, parallel conductors of infinite length and negligible circular cross section placed one meter apart in a vacuum.

Resistance: The unit of measurement of resistance symbolized by "R" is the Ohm, named after German physicist Georg Simon Ohm. It is defined as an electrical resistance between two points of a conductor when a constant potential difference of 1 volt applied to these points, produces in the conductor a current of 1 Ampere, the conductor not being the seat of any electromotive force. The abbreviation for the value of the resistance quantity is expressed with the symbol Ω, a Greek alphabet.

As we explore the various relationships between these quantities, these symbols and units are important.

OHM's Law

The first and most important relationship between Current, Voltage, and Resistance is known as Ohm's Law, discovered by Georg Simon Ohm and published in his 1827 paper, The Galvanic Circuit Investigated Mathematically. Ohm's main discovery was that the amount of electric current through a metal conductor in a circuit is directly proportional to the voltage across it, for any given temperature. Ohm used a simple equation to describe the inter-relationships between voltage, current, and resistance.

   Ohm's Law describes the relationship between voltage and current in an ideal conductor.

It states that: "The potential difference (voltage) across an ideal conductor is proportional to the current through it". The constant of proportionality is called the "resistance", R expressed mathematically thus;

$$V \alpha I$$

And since Resistance is a constant quantity on every metallic conductor, it is mathematically expressed as the constant of proportionality thus;

$$V = I \times R$$

Using algebraic equations, we can derive two other variations of this formula for I and R as the subject of the formula thus;

$$I = V/R \text{ and } R = V/I$$

Practically, these equations are very relevant for both designing and analyzing electrical circuits. Let us see some examples below;

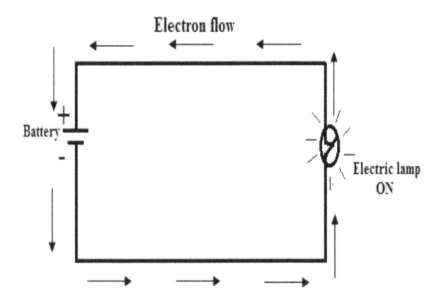

Figure 3.3a: Simple light bulb circuit

The light bulb circuit above presents us with a sample example. It has one source of voltage supply, the battery and one load - the light bulb - which is a resistance point for current flow in the circuit. When the value of any two of the three electrical quantities of voltage, current and resistance are known, Ohm's law can be used to determine the other missing value just like "find x" in algebra.

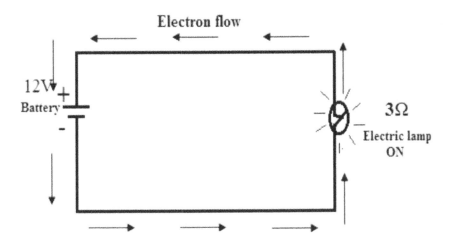

Figure 3.3b: Simple light bulb circuit

Supposing the source supply voltage is 12V and the resistance of the lamp is 3Ω,

Then using the formula V = IR, we substitute values thus;

12V = I x 3Ω

I = 12/3

I = 4A

The amount of current flowing in this circuit is 4A.

Likewise if we have a battery source of voltage, 16V and the current flowing in the circuit from the battery is 2A, then the unknown resistance of the lamp which serves as the load would be determined by;

R = V/I

$$R = 16/2$$

$$R = 8\Omega$$

What this means, is that if an underrated bulb of say 1.5A is used or the resistance in the circuit drops to 4 Ω, it will blow up.

The circuit was designed specifically to drive a current of 2A to the bulb. With a 4 Ω resistance, 4A will flow to it.

Also, the resistance of the load alone is not the total resistance in a circuit. All other sources of resistivity, like the intrinsic wire resistance are factored in when designing a circuit.

Ohm's law is a very simple and useful tool for circuit analysis. It is important for a technician to understand it and apply it mentally in the field.

Note that a voltage source such as a battery is a constant voltage source. It will therefore provide a constant voltage equivalent to its rated output, regardless of current. It is not the battery which determines the amount of current flowing in the circuit to the load, rather a combination of the load resistance and the operating voltage determines Current.

Voltage

Voltage is defined as the difference in electric potential energy between two points per unit electric charge. The voltage between these two points is equivalent to the work done per unit of charge against a static electric field to move that charge between two points and is measured in Volts (a joule per coulomb).

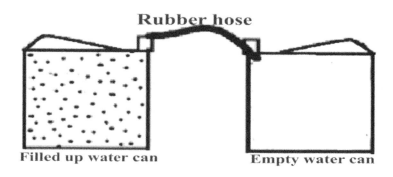

Figure 3.4a: Voltage Illustration

Voltage can be created by either a static electric field, electric current passing through a magnetic field; by time-varying magnetic fields, or some combination of these three processes. When voltage is applied between two points, one point usually has the presence of more charge than the other. In order to explain the concept of voltage, let us use the analogy of transferring water between two water cans as seen in figure 6.4a above.

Let;

Water = Charge (measured in Coulombs)
Pressure = Voltage (measured in Volts)
Flow = Current (measured in Amperes, or "Amps" for short)
Pipe Width = Resistance
In fig. 6.4a above, when the water in the can is sucked into the pipe and transferred to the empty can, a pressure difference between the two ends drives the flow of water along the pipe into the empty can. However, when both cans are placed on the same ground level or surface level, there will be no sustained flow. Therefore to create a potential difference between both cans, the can with water (source of charge) would need to be placed at a higher elevation as seen in fig. 6.4b.

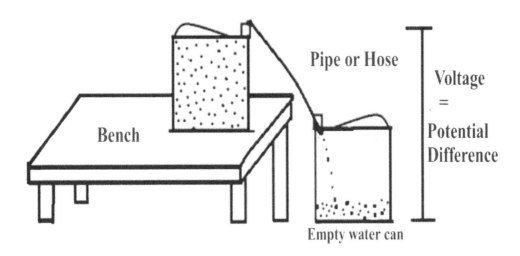

Figure 3.4b: Voltage Illustration

The pressure at the base of the pipe in the empty water can represent voltage. The water in the tank represents charge. The more water there is in the filled can, the higher the charge and the more the pressure measured at the base of the pipe in the empty can as water flows down.

We can think of the full water can as a battery source where a certain amount of energy is stored and then released. If we drain the full can by a certain amount, the pressure created at the base of the pipe in the empty can goes down. This is likened to a decrease in voltage. There is also a corresponding decrease in the amount of water that will flow through the pipe. A lower pressure would mean that less water will flow.

Voltage is defined in such a way as to suggest that negatively charged objects are pulled towards higher voltages, while positively charged objects are pulled towards lower voltages. Therefore, the "conventional current" in a wire or resistor always flow from higher voltage to lower voltage. More than just a continuous path (circuit) therefore, is needed before a continuous flow of electrons will occur in a circuit. Some kind of means or force is required to push electrons around the circuit and this is the very function of voltage in a circuit. With electrons, the influencing force for their directional flow around a circuit is the same force at work in static electricity which is produced by an imbalance of electric charge. That kind of imbalance is similar to what took place in this example of the two water cans above.

Current

Going back to our example of the two water cans, we can think of the amount of water flowing through the pipe from the full can as current. As the pressure increases, water flow increases as well and vice-versa. With water, we would measure the volume flowing through the pipe over a certain period of time. But with electricity, we measure the amount of charge flowing through the circuit over a period of time.

Therefore, Current is defined as the rate of charge flow past a given point in an electric circuit, measured in Coulombs per second (c/s) or Amperes. In electric circuits this charge is often carried by moving electrons in a wire. It can also be carried by ions in an electrolyte (Chemical mix), or by both ions and electrons as seen in batteries. Electric current can either be alternating (AC) or direct current (DC).

Alternating Current (AC): Alternating current is the movement of electric charge in such a way that the charged electrons periodically reverse direction. AC is the type of electric current used for supply of electric energy to consumer premises.

Direct Current (DC): Direct current however is the flow of electric charge in a uniform direction. Direct current is produced by sources such as batteries, thermocouples, solar cells etc. Direct current can flow in a conductor such as a copper wire, but it can also flow through semiconductors, insulators, or even through a vacuum as in electron or ion beams. The electric charge flows in a constant uniform direction, which is different from alternating current AC.

Resistance

A measure of the opposition to the flow of electrical charge or the degree to which a conductor opposes an electric current through that conductor is what is known as electrical resistance. The opposite is electrical conductance.

Electric circuits are designed to maximally utilize the energy injected into it by a voltage source without harm to the circuit components. If there is no resistance to current flow from a source to the circuit, the magnitude of current may be destructive to some components of the circuit especially if a high quantum of energy is released, in the form of heat. The resistance serves to limit the amount of current through the circuit with a given amount of voltage supplied by the battery or other voltage source.

Conductors are materials that have very low resistance while insulators are materials which possess very high or infinite resistance.

Resistance is measured in ohms represented by the symbol, Ω. According to ohm's law;

Resistance;

R = V/I

Power

Power is a measure of the work done in a given amount of time. It is a measure of the speed at which a standard amount of work is done. Besides voltage, current and resistance, power is a derived quantity as a result of the combination of voltage and current. In electric circuits, power is derived as a function of both voltage and current expressed as;

P = EI or P = VI

Where P = Power, E (or V) = Potential difference, Electromotive force or Voltage and I = Current. The unit of measurement of power is Watts (W).

Voltage is the specific work (or potential energy) per unit charge, while current is the rate at which electric charges move through a conductor. Combined as a product (multiplication), voltage (work) and current (rate) constitute power as an output.

A circuit with high voltage and low current might be dissipating the same amount of power as a circuit with low voltage and high current. Neither the amount of voltage alone nor the amount of current alone indicates the amount of power in an electric circuit. For instance, if a circuit is an open circuit, voltage would be present between the terminals of the source while current is zero; hence the power output will be zero. There would be no power dissipated, no matter how great that voltage might be.

Since, **P= I x E and I = 0, any value x 0 = 0**

Therefore, the power dissipated in any open circuit must be zero. Similarly, if we have a short circuit created with a pure metallic conductor cable (with absolutely zero resistance), there will be current in the loop with zero voltage, so likewise no power would be dissipated.

Since **P=IE** and **E=0, any value multiplied by 0 = 0**

Therefore, the power dissipated in a superconducting loop must be zero.

The formula for calculating power can further be derived mathematically thus;

P = VI, since from ohms' law **V = IR,**
Therefore, P = (IR) x I; so **P = I²R**
Or since I = V/R
P = V x (V/R); so **P = V²/ R**

Electronic Components, Functions and Uses

There are various discrete electronic components. They are used in almost all implementations of electronic circuitry which constitutes the internal electronics of various devices like radio, TV, computers, mobile smartphones, and telecommunication equipment, used in all fields of human endeavor.

These utility devices and equipment all share a common anatomy in internal circuit-board composition. The difference between one electronic device, gadget or equipment from another is in the circuit-board design (the arrangement of its discrete electronic components) tailored towards a specific purpose. Therefore, the purpose of a device determines its circuit-board design.

What this means for a technician is that a sound foundational understanding of electronics technology at a basic level is a key element in expert-level mastery and performance in the field.

While an engineer studies at a deeper level to produce complex electrical or electronic designs, a technician defined as someone who studies, or practices technology should implement designs, maintain designs, and correct faults in the design whenever it occurs.

Discrete electronic components are the opposite of their counterparts in the circuit board - the integrated circuits (ICs). They are distinct, separate electronic components.

Description of Discrete Electronic Components

The following basic components are found on the PCB of all electronic devices, including the PCBs of mobile smartphones and tablets which are our primary focus in this book. They include the following;

  a. Resistors
  b. Capacitors
  c. Inductors
  d. Transistors
  e. Diodes

Whenever I teach basic electronics, particularly on the subject of resistors and capacitors, I try to use an analogy about a farmer using a plot of land for mixed product farming and borehole for irrigation.
In like manner is a carved plate of circuit-board used for electronic product design. Such an example may not be a perfect one that captures all the intricacies or actions taking place in a working powered-up circuit-board but it would help a reader understand the concept to an extent I hope.

The water supply from a borehole or any water supply source serves to represent the power source for current flow to all components in the circuit-board. Pipes are laid for water to flow to each section of the farm just like the wire tracks on the printed circuit board.

Assuming the farmer segmented the farm into sections for Rice farming, Animal husbandry (Horses, Sheep and goats, cows and maybe poultry), corn and millet section etcetera, the same way is the motherboard of a phone or other electronic board, sectioned into final sub-circuits such as; the display unit, speaker, ringer, microphone, etc. Each of these final sub-circuits are compartments with similar discrete electronic components like the others, different only in its purposeful design (arrangement of the components) based on the current and voltage requirements of associated components. Sometimes a final sub-circuit would be integrated into a whole chip (integrated circuit, IC) aggregating the functions of the discrete electronic components into one whole unit.

Also, assume that for the purposes of this illustration, the main focus is how to get water circulated and shared to each section of the farm according to need. For instance, the water requirements for the rice section would be much more compared to the requirement for maize. The water requirement for goats and poultry will definitely be small compared to that of the horses or cows, as well as the frequency and timing of supply to each section. The same way it is with an electronic circuit-board design. Resistors serve to limit the flow of current and even set current at specific points in the circuit. If you relate it to our farm, an irrigation farmer who turns on the water at a central point in the farm with pipes circulating to the various sections will have to install various pipe dimensions according to need as well as stop corks at the entry point closer to each section. The bigger the pipe (low resistance), the higher the volume of water supplied to a section and vice versa. Stop corks (representing variable resistance) may also serve to further regulate flow to areas where it is needed to flow slowly, faster or even stopped completely. These can be equated to the resistor's ability to regulate and control flow of current in a circuit. Another component of importance is the capacitor.

In DC circuits, capacitors act to store charges albeit temporarily and also discharge the stored charges, block DC current, pass or filter AC currents etc. The main purpose of a capacitor in DC circuits is to filter out any AC component that enters into the system by providing a low impedance path for them to flow out of the circuit. It also acts as a reservoir of energy by maintaining almost a constant DC voltage across its plates. The unwanted AC components can either be noise,   ripples, unwanted radio frequency signals or any alternating signal caused by a combination of components on the circuit-board which can corrupt the required pure DC signals.

What capacitors filter in a circuit is dependent on how these components are combined in the circuit. For instance, if you connect a capacitor in series with a parallel resistor, it will pass AC signals but a resistor connected in series with a parallel capacitor-to-ground connection will filter the AC component out of the circuit.

Going back to our farm analogy, a farmer can place storage cans in each section of the farm or some sections like those for cows, poultry, horses etc. for times when the central tap is not supplying water. Equate it to our DC circuit; we have such distributed temporary storage across every electronic circuit and the storage elements are capacitors.

Capacitors are used on circuit boards to serve as a local energy store for most of the very high frequency devices. As you know there are many devices on a motherboard just like the farm, trying to draw power from the power supply. This will not be energy efficient just as it will be a burden, always going to turn on the water just for poultry or just because water in one section of a farm has become exhausted. With the capacitors in every final sub-circuit, energy is therefore drawn from each storage capacitor located nearest to that device's sub-circuit just like each section's storage water cans placed by the farmer. If we relate other applications of capacitors such as filtering unwanted signals, remember that waste cans or filtration cans do exist also in farms or water distribution systems.

Therefore, high frequency components' immediate power requirements are drawn from nearby capacitors. The capacitors replenish their charge storage from the power supply and other capacitors too. The main power supply is the battery for mobile smartphones and the power supply units of other electronic devices, while the main local storage capacitors found in various DC circuits are the electrolytic capacitors.

Electrolytic capacitors are the polarized versions of capacitors found in electronic circuits. It means their terminals have polarity (marked + and -). They are unidirectional with high impedance and therefore not used for high frequency current scenarios. Other non-electrolytic capacitors used in circuits are bidirectional with low impedance which is suitable for high frequency components application.

Let us look at these components individually in the sections below.

Resistors

Resistors are the most fundamental and commonly used of all the discrete electronic components. The principal job of a resistor within an electrical or electronic circuit is to "resist" (from which the name, "Resistor" was derived). So primarily, a resistor does the following;

- Regulates the flow of electrons or current;

- Impedes or sets the flow of electrons or current through a particular path;

- Impose a voltage reduction in an electrical circuit.

Resistors are referred to as "Passive Devices" which means that they have no intrinsic source of power or amplification but only reduces the voltage or current signal passing through them. Passive devices also have linear characteristics as they experience voltage drops across them when current flows through their terminals. The reduction process results in loss of electrical energy in the form of heat as the resistor resists the flow of electrons through it. Therefore, for current to pass through its terminals from an external power source, a potential difference is required between the two terminals of a resistor. This potential difference balances out the energy lost.

When it is used in DC circuits, a voltage drop is measured across its terminals as the circuit current flows through the resistor.

In obedience to Ohm's Law, different values of resistance produces different values of current or voltage.

This makes resistors very useful in electronic circuits where they control or reduce either the current flow or voltage produced across them. Resistors can also be either "Fixed or Variable" resistors. Fixed resistors have one single value of resistance only. A 10Ω resistor is an example of a fixed resistor because it has a fixed value of 10. Variable resistors (potentiometers) on the other hand can provide an infinite number of resistance values between zero and a maximum value. There are many different types of resistors available for the electronics design engineer to choose from. There are the very small surface-mount chip resistors and as well the large wire-wound power resistors. Sizes and applications may differ.

Surface mount resistors are the resistor types used in mobile smartphones. Typically, this type of resistor is manufactured using thin-film technology. Surface mount resistors are rectangular in shape, having metalized edges at either end of the body through which they make contact with the printed circuit board using solder. They are made by depositing a metal-oxide film on a ceramic substrate. The resistance property is determined by the thickness and the length of the metal oxide film.

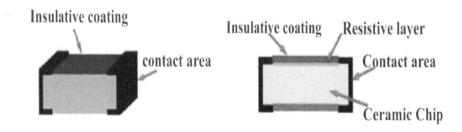

Figure 3.5:Surface Mount Resistor design structure
Credit: http://www.radioelectronics.com/info/data/resistor/smd_resistor/smd_resistor.php

The surface mount resistor terminations (the metalized edges) are very important especially during soldering. They need to make a good reliable contact with the resistive element of the chip resistor. If it gets broken off or corroded, it will not function.

Temperature Coefficient: When working on these types of resistors especially using hot air stations or soldering irons, care must be taken as regards their temperature coefficient characteristics.

Temperature coefficient is a coefficient expressing the relationship between a change in their physical property and the change in temperature that causes it. The use of metal-oxide film enables these SMD resistors to provide a good temperature coefficient with values ranging from 25, 50 up to 100 ppm/°C in use.

Symbols: The symbol used in both schematic and electrical drawings for a Resistor can either be a rectangular box or a "zig-zag" type line.

Figure 3.6a: Schematic symbol of Resistors

Resistors Circuit Connections

Resistors are connected within electrical or electronic circuits either in "Series" or in "Parallel" or the combination of both.

Resistors in Series

Resistors are connected in "Series" when they are daisy-chained together in a single line. Series-connected resistors have a common current flowing through them.

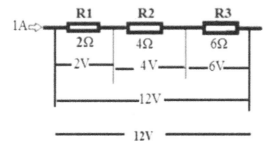

Fig. 3.6b: Resistors in Series

Mathematically, this can be represented as;

$I_T = I_1 = I_2 = I_3....I_n$ where I_T is the total current, while the total circuit resistance of series resistors is;

$R_T = R_1 + R_2 + R_3...+ R_n$ where R_T is the total circuit resistance of the series resistors.

The total voltage is also the sum of the individual voltage drops across each resistor;

$V_T = V_1 + V_2 + V_3...+ V_n$ where V_T is the total voltage drop.

The value in ohms of the total resistance of a series connected circuit will always be greater than the resistor of highest value within the series.

From the diagram above, we see that the combined resistance of the three resistors is 12Ω. It means that all three resistors can be changed with a single 12 Ω resistor.

The Voltage Divider Circuit

We can see from the above example that, assuming the supply voltage is 12 volts, different voltages or voltage drops would (I x R) appear across each resistor within the series network. When resistors are connected in series this way, across a single DC supply, the main advantage is that different reference voltage values appear across each resistor producing a kind of circuit known as the Voltage Divider Network.

This simple circuit shares the supply voltage proportionally across each resistor in the series link with the amount of voltage drop being determined by the resistors' value. From what we have learnt, the current through a series resistor circuit is common to all resistors present. So a higher value resistance will have a higher voltage drop across it, while a smaller value resistance will have a smaller voltage drop across it.

The series resistive circuit shown above forms a simple voltage divider network where three voltages 2V, 4V and 6V are produced from a single 12V supply. Kirchhoff's Voltage Law states that "*the supply voltage in a closed circuit is equal to the sum of all the voltage drops (IR) around the circuit*" and this can be used to good effect.

The Voltage Divider Rule, allows the design engineer to use the effects of resistance proportionality to calculate the potential difference across each resistor regardless of the current flowing through the series circuit.

A typical "voltage divider circuit" is shown below.

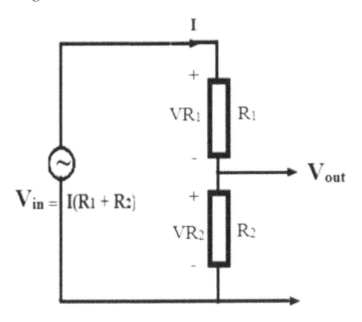

Fig. 3.6c: Resistor as a Voltage Divider circuit

In the circuit shown above, two resistors, R1 and R2 are connected together in series across the supply voltage **Vin**. One side of the power supply voltage is connected to resistor, R1 and the voltage output, **Vout** is taken from across resistor **R2**. The value of this output voltage is given by the formula below.

$$\textbf{Vout} = \textbf{Vin} \left(\frac{\textbf{R}_2}{\textbf{R1} + \textbf{R2}} \right)$$

Assuming more resistors are series-connected in the circuit, then different voltages will be present across each resistor according to their individual resistance R values, providing different but smaller voltage points from one single supply in obedience to Ohms Law where;

$$V = I \times R$$

So if we had three or more resistances in the series chain, we can still use our now familiar potential divider formula to find the voltage drop across each one. Consider the circuit below.

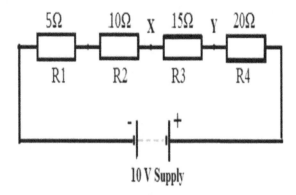

Example 3.1: Resistor as Voltage Divider calculation

To calculate the voltage across point X and Y (i.e. resistor R3), we use the same potential divider (or voltage divider) formula;

$$V_{XY} = VR3 = V_{supply} X \quad \frac{R3}{R1+R2+R3+R4}$$

$$V_{XY} = 10x \quad \frac{15}{5+10+15+20}$$

$$= 10x\ 0.3$$

$$V_{XY} = VR3 = 3V$$

Let us evaluate another circuit to drive home the various ways a series resistor circuit can impact an electronic design. Look at this diagram below;

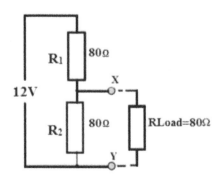

Example 3.2: Resistor as Voltage Divider calculation

Assuming we have an existing circuit like the voltage divider circuit above and a component, say a speaker (RLoad) is tapping power from this circuit with a load resistance (or impedance) of 80Ω. The circuit is designed to supply an input voltage to this speaker not exceeding 6V. Potential divider circuits like this enabled a design like this, which produces a smaller voltage (in this case 6V) from a larger supply voltage (in this case 12V).

With a 12V DC supply as in the circuit above;

The voltage drops across X and Y is calculated thus;

    i.   Without the speaker (RLoad) connected
   ii.   With speaker (RLoad) connected

For (i): where R(x-y) = 80Ω; Output Voltage Vo; Input Voltage Vi;

$$V_0 = V_{in} \times \frac{R_2}{R_1 + R_2}$$

$$V_0 = 12 \times \frac{80}{80 + 80}$$

Vo = 6V across R2 when no load is connected in parallel to R2.

When the load (Speaker) is connected however, the combined parallel load at x-y will become 40Ω.

$$\frac{80 \times 80}{80 + 80} = 40\,\Omega$$

Therefore, the reference circuit output supply voltage to the speaker will be;

$$V_0 = 12 \times \frac{40}{80 + 40}$$

$$V_0 = 12 \times 0.33$$

Vo = 4V.

Testing the terminals of the speaker should give you the above value.

The above example also shows that connecting two equal value resistors, of say 80Ω each, together as a potential divider network across the 12V produced a reduced lower voltage of 6Veffectively until we connected the load circuit to the network. The effect of resistor RLoad connected in parallel across R2 changes the ratio of the two series resistances thereby altering their voltage drop.

We can therefore see that a loaded voltage divider network changes its output voltage as a result of this loading effect, since the output voltage Vout, is determined by the ratio of R1 to R2. In a situation whereby the load is a variable resistor as the load resistance, RL increases towards infinity (∞); this loading effect reduces and the Voltage ratio of Vout/Vs will not be affected by additional load on the output. Therefore the higher the load impedance, the lower the loading effect on the output.

With this knowledge, a technician can troubleshoot final sub-circuits of peripheral components by checking reference voltage test points.

Resistors in Parallel

When resistors are connected in such a way that they have both sides of their respective terminals connected to each of the equivalent side terminal of another resistor or resistors, they are said to be connected in parallel.

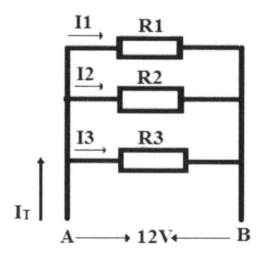

Figure 3.6d: Resistors in Parallel

The total resistance of a parallel circuit is mathematically represented below and the total resistance of a parallel circuit will always be less than the value of the smallest resistor. Unlike the series resistors, the sum of the reciprocal of parallel resistors gives the equivalent total resistor value;

$$\frac{1}{R_T} = \frac{1}{R_1} + \frac{1}{R_2} + \frac{1}{R_3} + \frac{1}{R_n}$$

But where the two resistances (or impedances) in parallel are equal and of the same value, then the total or equivalent resistance, R_T is equal to half the value of one resistor i.e.;

R/2 for two resistors; R/3 for three equal resistors in parallel etcetera.

Parallel resistors have a common voltage across them where total supply voltage is;

$$V_s = V_1 = V_2 = V_3 .... = V_n$$

Total circuit current flow is equal to the sum of all the individual branch currents added together as below;

$$I_T = I_1 + I_2 + I_3 ... + I_n$$

Other ways resistors can be connected in parallel are as shown below;

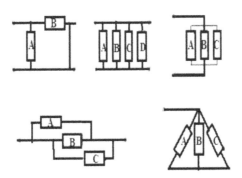

Figure 3.6e: Other Resistors in Parallel circuits

Let us do a little calculation with the following diagram below

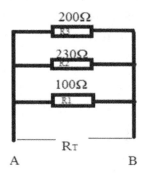

Example 3.3: Parallel Circuit calculation

To calculate R_T, the total equivalent resistance of the three parallel resistors;

$1/\ R_T = 1/R1 + 1/R2 + 1/R3$
$1/\ R_T = 1/100 + 1/230 + 1/200$
$1/\ R_T = 0.01 + 0.004 + 1/0.005$
$1/\ R_T = 0.019$
$R_T = 1/0.019$
$R_T = 52.63\Omega$

This method above applies to any number of resistors connected in parallel. The formula for calculating **two** resistors in parallel is;

$$R_T\ =\ \frac{R1\ x\ R2}{R1 + R2}$$

Current in Parallel Resistors

The total current, I_T in a parallel resistor circuit is the sum of the individual currents flowing in all branches of the parallel circuit. The amount of current flowing in each parallel branch is not necessarily the same. This is because the value of the resistance in each branch determines the current within that branch. For example, although the parallel combination has the same constant voltage across it, the resistances could be of different values; hence the current flowing through each resistor would definitely be different based on Ohms Law. Consider the three resistors in parallel above.

The current that flows through each of the resistors (I_{R1}, I_{R2} and I_{R3}) connected together in parallel is not necessarily the same value as it depends on the resistive value of the resistor.

However, we do know that the current that enters the circuit at point A must also exit the circuit at point B.

Recall that Kirchhoff's Current Law states that: "*the total current leaving a circuit is equal to that entering the circuit – no current is lost*". Thus, the total current flowing in the circuit is given as:

$$I_T = I_{R1} + I_{R2} + I_{R3}$$

Then by using Ohm's Law, where **V = IR**

And V_S = Supply voltage = 12V

I_{Rx}, the current flowing through each resistor of the above diagram can be calculated as:

The Current flowing through R1, I_{R1} = V_S ÷ **R1**
I_{R1} = 12V ÷ 100Ω = 0.12A

The Current flowing through R2, I_{R2} = V_S ÷ **R2**

I_{R2} = 12V ÷ 230Ω = 0.05A and

The Current flowing through R3, I_{R3} = V_S ÷ **R3**

I_{R3} = 12V ÷ 200Ω = 0.06A
Thus giving us a total current I_T flowing around the circuit as:

I_T = 0.12A + 0.05A + 0.06A = **0.23A**
This result can also be verified directly using Ohm's Law as:

I_T = V_S ÷ R_T = 12 ÷ 52.63Ω = 0.228 approximately **0.23A** (the same)

The equation given for calculating the total current flowing in a parallel resistor circuit which is the sum of all the individual currents added together is given as:

$$I_T = I_1 + I_2 + I_3... + I_n$$

Also, parallel resistor networks can be thought of as "current dividers" because the supply current divides between the various parallel branches. So a parallel resistor circuit having 'N' number of resistive networks will have N-different current paths while maintaining a common voltage across itself. Parallel resistors can also be interchanged with each other without changing the total resistance or the total circuit current.

Resistors in AC Circuits

In the previous sections on the behavior and design calculations for resistors in series and parallel circuits, the assumption was that both the voltage and current had a constant polarity, flow and direction.

This is the nature of DC current or circuits and applicable to mobile phone circuits. In this section however, we shall briefly examine the other type of electricity supply known as AC or Alternating current.

AC voltages usually switch polarity from positive to negative and back again over time, and the current with respect to the voltage swings back and forth. The oscillating shape of an AC supply follows that of the mathematical form of a "sine wave" which is commonly called a Sinusoidal Waveform. Therefore, a sinusoidal voltage can be defined mathematically thus;

$$V(t) = Vmax\ sin\ \omega t.$$

The usual Ohm's law and Kirchoff's laws for calculating voltage, current and power quantities applies when a resistive DC circuit is designed with pure resistors that possess negligible presence of inductance and capacitance.

But when dealing with AC circuits, peak-to-peak values of these quantities or their root mean square are considered in the calculations. So when using resistors in AC circuits, the term Impedance, symbol Z is the generally used alphabet and we can say that;

$$DC\ resistance = AC\ impedance,\ R = Z.$$

Resistors are "passive" devices because they do not produce or consume any electrical energy, but convert electrical energy into heat. In AC circuits, factors such as the frequency and phase difference or phase angle (φ) of the supply voltage affects the application of Ohms' law calculation for R. A resistor will always have the same resistance value no matter what the supply frequency is, from low to very high frequencies unlike capacitors and inductors. When resistors are used in AC circuits the direction of the current flowing through them has no effect on the behavior of the resistor so it will rise and fall as the voltage rises and falls. The current and voltage reaches maximum, fall through zero and reach minimum at exactly the same time. This means that they rise and fall simultaneously and are said to be "in-phase".

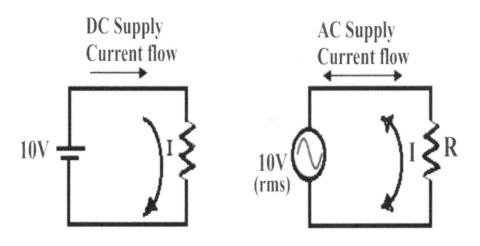

Figure 3.7: Current flow direction in DC and AC circuits

Phase Relationship Diagram for Voltage and Current in AC circuits

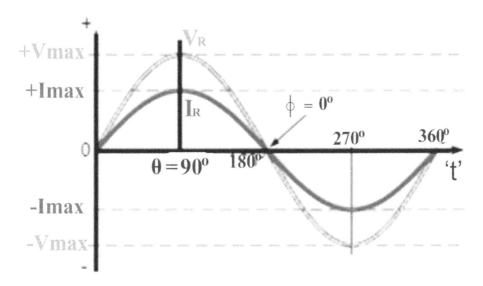

Graph 3.1: V-I Phase Relationship

On a Cartesian coordinate, representation of a sinusoid depicts its cyclic nature and explains the phase relationship between current and voltage. From the diagram above, at any point along the horizontal x-axis the instantaneous voltage and current are both in-phase because the current and the voltage reach their maximum values at the same time when their phase angle θ is 0o. Then these instantaneous values of voltage and current can be compared to give the value of the resistance in ohms by using Ohm's law.

Capacitors

A capacitor is a passive two-terminal electrical component used to store electrical energy temporarily in an electric field. In a way, a capacitor is a little like a battery. Although they function in completely different ways, capacitors and batteries both store electrical energy.

Whenever an electrical voltage exists between two parallel separated conductors, an electric field becomes present within the space between those conductors. Electric Fields are invisible electromagnetic forces surrounding an area which influences the properties of materials that exist within that area.

A Capacitor is basically made of two or more parallel conductive (metal) plates which are not connected to each other, but are electrically separated either by air or by what is called a dielectric. Dielectrics used can be insulating materials such as waxed paper, mica, ceramic, plastic or a liquid gel as used in electrolytic capacitors.

Figure 3.8a: Symbol of a Capacitor

There are different kinds of capacitors available. They are usually named according to the material used in making them. No matter the type of capacitor used in a circuit, they all store electric charge. The conductive metal plates of a capacitor can take the form of a square, circle or rectangle. Also, the general shape, size and construction of a parallel plate capacitor depends on its application and voltage rating.

When capacitors are used in a DC circuit, they charge up to the source supply voltage while blocking the flow of current through them. This is due to the dielectric of a capacitor which is non-conductive and basically an insulator. But when a capacitor is connected to an AC circuit, current flows through the capacitor with little or no resistance to the flow.

When voltage is applied to the plates of a capacitor, the plates are charged up and these charges continue to build up at the plates until the voltage across the plates are equal to that of the supply voltage.

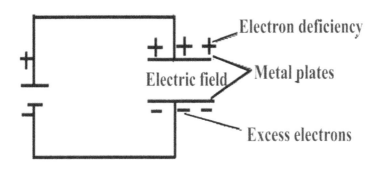

Figure 3.8b: Effect of voltage across the parallel plates of a Capacitor

The Capacitance of a Capacitor

Capacitance is an electrical property of a capacitor and is the measure of a capacitor's ability to store electrical charge on its two plates with the unit of capacitance being the Farad (F), named after the British physicist Michael Faraday.

A capacitor has the capacitance of One Farad when a charge of One Coulomb is stored on the plates by a voltage of One volt. Capacitance, C is always positive and has no negative units. Capacitors do eventually lose their stored charges due to internal leakage paths for electrons to flow from one plate to the other. Depending on the specific type of capacitor, the time it takes for a stored charge voltage to discharge can be a long time.

When the voltage across a capacitor is increased from low to higher levels, it is said to be charging because there is an increasing amount of energy being stored in its electric field. Therefore it draws current from the rest of the circuit, acting as a power load.

In this condition the direction of flow of electrons with regard to the voltage polarity is from the negative to the positive terminal.

The Capacitor absorbs energy from the circuit

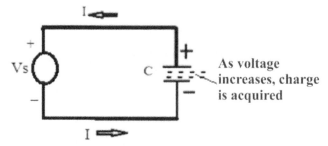

Figure 3.8c: When the capacitor is charging

The reverse is the case when the voltage across a capacitor is decreased, the capacitor supplies current to the rest of the circuit, acting as a power source. In this condition the capacitor is said to be *discharging*. Its store of energy (held in the electric field) is decreasing as energy is released to the rest of the circuit.

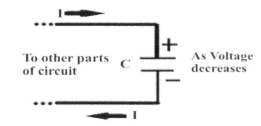

Figure 3.8d: When the Capacitor is discharging

Both scenarios above serve to illustrate the behavior of capacitors in the circuit. If a source of voltage is suddenly applied to an uncharged capacitor (which implies a sudden increase in voltage), the capacitor would draw current from that source, absorbing energy from it, until the capacitor's voltage equals that of the source. But once the capacitor voltage reaches a fully charged state, its stored charge will decay to zero.

On the other hand, if a load resistance is connected to a charged capacitor, the capacitor would supply current to that load until all its stored energy is released and its voltage decays to zero. Once the capacitor voltage is completely discharged, its current decays to zero. Because of this inherent ability to be charged and then discharged, capacitors can be thought of as acting somewhat like batteries.

Capacitors in Series

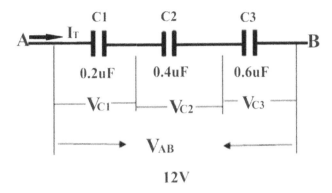

Figure 3.8e: Capacitors in Series

When capacitors are connected together in a daisy-chain with its second terminal (plate) connected to the first terminal (plate) of another capacitor, it is considered to be in series. This series connection means that in a DC connected circuit as n fig. 3.8e above, capacitor C2 is effectively isolated from the circuit, sandwiched between C1 and C3. The outcome of this is that the effective plate area decreases to the smallest individual capacitance connected in the series chain. Therefore, the voltage drop across each capacitor will be different depending upon the values of the individual capacitances. If we apply Kirchhoff's Voltage Law to the circuit above;

$V_{AB} = V_{C1} + V_{C2} + V_{C3} = 12V$

Where Q_T = total charge

$V_{C1} = Q_T / C1$, $V_{C2} = Q_T / C2$ and $V_{C3} = Q_T / C3$

$V_{AB} = Q_T / C_T = Q_T / C1 + Q_T / C2 + Q_T / C3$

If we divide each term by Q we have;

$1/ C_T = 1/C_1 + 1/C_2 + 1/C_3 +... 1/C_n$ as the series capacitor equation.

To calculate the total capacitance for two capacitors in series however, we use;

$$C_T = \frac{C_1 \times C_2}{C_1 + C_2}$$

With series-connected resistors, the sum of all the voltage drops across the series circuit will be equal to the applied voltage V_S (Kirchhoff's Voltage Law). This is true about capacitors in series as well. With series-connected capacitors, the capacitive reactance of the capacitor acts as impedance due to the frequency of the supply. This capacitive reactance produces a voltage drop across each capacitor. Therefore, series connected capacitors act as a capacitive voltage divider network like their resistor counterparts. Consequently, the voltage divider formula applied to resistors can also be used to find the individual voltages for two capacitors in series.

Where C_X is the capacitance of the capacitor in question, V_S is the supply voltage across the series chain and V_{CX} is the voltage drop across the target capacitor, then;

$$V_{CX} = \frac{V_S \times C_T}{C_X}$$

Capacitors in Parallel

When capacitors are connected in parallel, they have a common voltage supply across them.

$$V_{AB} = V_S = V_1 = V_2 = V_3 = 12V$$

C1, C2 and C3 are all connected together in a parallel branch between points A and B as shown below;

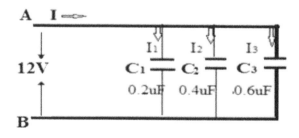

Example 3.4: Capacitors in Parallel calculation

When Capacitors are connected together in parallel the total or equivalent capacitance, C_T in the circuit is equal to the sum of all the individual capacitors added together.

$$C_T = C_1 + C_2 + C_3 + \ldots C_n$$

$$C_T = 0.2uF + 0.4uF + 0.6uF$$

$$C_T = 1.2uF \text{ (microfarad)}$$

One important point to remember about parallel connected capacitor circuits is; the total capacitance (C_T) of any two or more capacitors connected together in parallel will always be GREATER than the value of the largest capacitor in the group. This is because we are adding together values.

When three, four or more capacitors are connected together the total capacitance of the circuit C_T would still be the sum of all the individual capacitors added together. This is because the total surface area of the plates has been increased. If we connect two identical capacitors, the surface areas of the plates will double thereby doubling the capacitance of the combination.

Capacitors in AC Circuits

When we apply an alternating current or AC supply across the plates of a capacitor, the capacitor will alternately charge and discharge at a rate determined by the frequency of the supply. The Capacitance of a capacitor in AC circuits change as the supply frequency changes while the capacitor is being constantly charged and discharged. This is unlike in DC circuits where they become charged to the value of the source voltage behaving like temporary storage devices and maintain the charge indefinitely as long as the supply voltage is present.

The flow of electrons onto the plates of a Capacitor is directly proportional to the rate of change of the voltage across those plates. Capacitors in AC circuits pass current through them when the voltage across its plates is constantly changing with respect to time (sinusoidal AC signals), but they block current flow through them when the voltage is a constant DC signals. Therefore, Capacitance in AC circuits varies with frequency as the capacitor is being constantly charged and discharged.

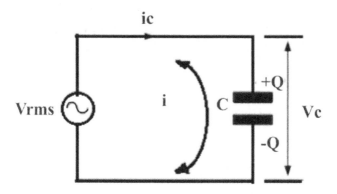

Figure 3.8f: Capacitor in AC circuit

In the circuit above, the capacitor is connected directly across the AC supply voltage. This example is a purely capacitive circuit with zero effects of any other connected components. As the supply voltage increases and decreases, the capacitor charges and discharges respectively with changing voltage. Since the charging current is directly proportional to the rate of change of the voltage across the plates of the capacitor, this rate of change is at its greatest as the supply voltage crosses over from its positive half-cycle to its negative half-cycle or vice versa at points 0° and 180° along the sine wave when plotted on a graph.

The smallest change in voltage occurs when the AC sine wave crosses over at its maximum or minimum peak voltage level, (Vm). At these positions in the cycle the maximum or minimum currents are flowing through the capacitor circuit and this is shown in the graph below.

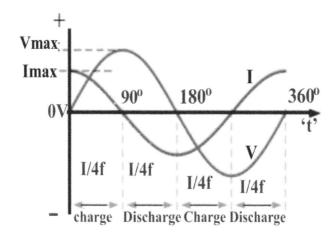

Graph 3.2: Capacitor Phasor diagram for AC circuits

Capacitive Reactance

Capacitive Reactance in a purely capacitive circuit is the opposition to current flow only in AC circuits. Like resistance, reactance is also measured in Ohms but is given the symbol X to distinguish it from a purely resistive value. Since reactance is a quantity that can also be applied to Inductors as well as Capacitors, when used with capacitors it is more commonly known as Capacitive Reactance.

For capacitors in AC circuits, capacitive reactance is given the symbol Xc. Therefore, capacitive reactance is defined as a capacitor's resistive value that varies with frequency.

Finally Capacitors, like all electrical components, have certain limitations which must be respected for the sake of reliability and proper circuit operation. For instance, capacitors are made of two conductors separated by an insulator (the dielectric), so its maximum voltage must not be exceeded. If excessive voltage is applied, the "breakdown" rating of the dielectric material might be exceeded, resulting in the capacitor internally short-circuiting. Also, some capacitors are manufactured in such a way that they can tolerate applied voltage in one polarity but not the other due to their construction.

Inductors

An Inductor, also called a coil is a passive two-terminal electrical component which resists **changes** in electric **current** passing through it. Note that it doesn't resist the flow of current like resistors, but changes in current. It consists of a conductor such as a wire, usually wound into a coil. Energy is stored in a magnetic field in the coil as long as current flows.

An inductor's opposition to AC current is based specifically on inductive reaction to changes in current, unlike in resistors which are based on friction. When alternating current flows through the windings of an inductor, the current flow represents increase in current through its windings so the inductor reacts to this increase by opposing it and when the current flow is decreasing, the inductor reverses polarity and reacts to oppose the decrease in current. So it actually reacts to <u>changes</u> in the current flow.

However, inductors are not quite pure in their reactive behavior. Firstly, they are made of wire wound conductors which means that they possess intrinsic resistance property.

Figure 3.9: Schematic Symbol of Inductors

The in-built resistance acts as though it were connected in series with a perfect inductance of the coil. Therefore, the impedance of any real inductor will always be a combination of resistance and inductive reactance where inductive reactance is the opposition that an inductor offers to alternating current due to its storage and release of energy in its magnetic field.

An inductor's opposition to change in current translates to an opposition to alternating current (AC) generally, which is by definition always changing in instantaneous magnitude and direction. This opposition to alternating current can be compared to that of resistance, but different in that it always results in a phase shift between current and voltage, and it dissipates zero power. Because of the differences, it has a different name – *reactance* symbolized by the capital letter "X" but measured in ohms just like resistance (R).

Since inductors drop voltage in proportion to the rate of change of current, they will drop more voltage for faster-changing current, and less voltage for slower-changing current therefore reactance in ohms for any inductor is directly proportional to the frequency of the alternating current.

Diodes

Diodes are basic unidirectional Semiconductor Devices that will only allow current to flow through them in one direction. The Signal Diode is the most basic active component in electronic circuits. Unlike resistors which are passive devices, a diode does not act in a linear manner with respect to the applied voltage as it has an exponential Current-Voltage relationship. This makes it difficult to analyze diodes using Ohm's law as is done for resistors.

Before we continue, let us understand the basic theory of semi-conductors of which diodes, transistors and even integrated circuit chips are made of.

Semi-conductors Basics

Semiconductor materials from Chemistry - the periodic table - such as silicon (Si) and Germanium (Ge) have electrical properties described between being part the properties of a "conductor" and that of an "insulator". They are neither good conductors nor good insulators hence their name "semi-conductors". The amount of "free electrons" in their atoms is closely grouped together in a crystalline pattern called a "crystal lattice".

However, the ability of semi-conductors to conduct electricity can be greatly improved by either replacing or adding certain donor or acceptor atoms to this crystalline structure in order to produce more free electrons (-) than holes (+) or vice versa. This is achieved by adding a small percentage of another element to the base material, either silicon or germanium.

Silicon and Germanium are classified as intrinsic semiconductors individually. This means that they are chemically pure, containing nothing but semi-conductive material. But if the amount of impurities added to this intrinsic semiconductor material is controlled, then its conductivity property can also be controlled.

Various impurities known as donors or acceptors can be added to this intrinsic material to produce free electrons or holes respectively. This process of adding donor or acceptor atoms to semiconductor atoms is known as *Doping*. When you "dope" Silicon, it loses its purity to become impure. This is because, any donor and acceptor atoms from another element is referred to as an "impurity", so by doping these silicon materials with a sufficient number of impurities, we can turn it into a semi-conductor, likewise Germanium etc.

Silicon is the most commonly used semiconductor basic material. That is the reason a place like the Southern California San Francisco Bay area is nick-named "Silicon Valley" because the word "silicon" originally referred to the large number of silicon chip innovators and manufacturers in the region. Silicon has four valence electrons in its outermost shell which it shares with its neighboring silicon atoms to fully form eight orbital electrons. The structure of the bond between the two silicon atoms is such that each atom shares one electron with its neighbor to stabilize the atomic bond. The arrangement of Silicon atoms is symmetrical in pattern making them a crystalline solid structure. Pure silica is generally an intrinsic crystal since it has no impurities, hence has no free electrons in its atomic structure. In order to extract electric current from a silicon crystal, we create a positive and a negative pole within the silicon allowing electrons to flow out of the silicon. This is achieved by doping. There are two types of semi-conductor materials:

N-type Semi-conductor

These are materials which have 5 valence electron-impurity atoms (Donors) added to them and conduct current by "electron" motion. They are therefore regarded as N-type Semiconductors.

A semiconductor material is classified as N-type when it has more electrons than holes (positive ions) making one of its poles a negative pole. In N-type semiconductors, the "donors" are positively charged with a large number of free electrons. The holes are smaller in number relative to the number of free electrons. When doping is applied, we have positively charged donors and negatively charged free electrons. But when you apply voltage across the terminals of the "doped" semiconductor in a way referred to as *biasing,* we have negatively charged free electrons and positively charged holes.

In order for a silicon crystal to conduct electricity, an impurity atom such as Antimony, Arsenic or Phosphorus has to be added into the crystalline structure making it extrinsic (impurities are added). These donor atoms have five outer electrons in their outermost orbital which they share with neighboring atoms. This is why they are commonly called "Pentavalent" impurities - ("Penta" equals to 5). Four out of the five orbital electrons will therefore bond with their neighboring silicon atoms leaving one "free electron" un-bonded. This free electron becomes mobile once an electrical voltage is applied, leading to electron flow. Antimony which is usually used is symbolized by Sb in the periodic table.

Since each impurity atom "donates" one electron, pentavalent atoms are generally known as "donors".

P-type Semiconductor

These are materials which have 3 valence electron-impurity atoms (Acceptors) added and conduct electric current by "hole" motion. They are therefore called P-type Semiconductors.

In P-type semi-conductor materials the "Acceptors" are negatively charged electrons and there are a large number of holes compared to small number of free electrons. When "doping" (addition of impurities) is applied, we have negatively charged acceptors and positively charged holes. When voltage is applied to its terminals after doping, we have positively charged holes and negatively charged free electrons.

Supposing a "Trivalent" (3-electron) impurity is added into the crystalline structure, such as Boron, Aluminum or Indium, which have only three valence electrons available in their outermost orbital, the fourth closed bond cannot be formed. Therefore, a complete connection is not possible, giving the semiconductor material an abundance of positively charged carriers known as "holes" in the structure of the crystal where electrons are effectively missing.

With the presence of a hole in the silicon crystal, a neighboring electron will be attracted to that hole such that it will try to fill it. By moving from its location to fill up the hole, the electron leaves another hole behind it. Another electron becomes attracted to the new hole, leaves to fill it and by so doing creates another hole behind. This goes on indefinitely in cycles making it look like a "holes movement", this time as a positive charge through the crystal structure.

This movement of holes results in a shortage of electrons in the silicon, turning the entire doped crystal into a positive pole. Since each impurity atom generates a hole, trivalent impurities are generally known as "Acceptors" as they are continually "accepting" extra electrons. P and N-type semiconductors are in general electrically neutral individually. Antimony (Sb) and Boron (B) are two of the most commonly used doping agents since they are more freely available compared to other types of materials. There are other chemical elements that can also be used as doping agents to a base material of either Silicon (S) or Germanium (Ge) to produce different types of basic semiconductor materials for use in electronic semiconductor components, microprocessors and solar cell applications. Diodes are semiconductors which consist of both N-type and P-type materials. There are two types of diodes based on their size;

- The Signal Diode and
- The Power Diode.

The Signal Diode is a very small sized non-linear semiconductor device generally used in electronic circuits where small currents or high frequencies are involved such as in smartphones, radio, television and digital logic circuits.

The Power Diode however is a bigger sized semiconductor device with larger forward-bias currents or higher reverse-bias blocking voltages. The PN junction of a small signal diode would eventually overheat and melt if used where higher voltages are involved so larger Power Diodes are used instead.

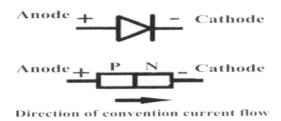

Figure 3.10a: Schematic Symbol of Diodes

The power semiconductor diode, known simply as the Power Diode, has a much larger PN junction area compared to the smaller signal diode, resulting in a high forward current capability and a high reverse blocking voltage. The electronic symbol for any type of diode is that of an arrow with a bar or line at its end as shown in fig.3.10a above.

Electron-flow direction as we have learnt from basic electricity principles is in the opposite direction to conventional current from cathode to anode. The arrow always points in the direction of conventional current flow through the diode, which suggests that the diode will only conduct if a positive terminal of the supply source is connected to the Anode and a negative terminal of the supply source is connected to the Cathode; consequently, allowing current to flow through it ONLY in one direction.

This is what is referred to as the Forward Biased condition.

However, if an external energy source is connected in the reverse direction, the diode will block any current from flowing through it and instead will act like an open switch. This is referred to as the Reversed Biased condition.

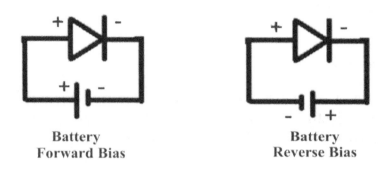

Figure 3.10b: Biasing of Diodes

To understand the concept of biasing a diode, let us discuss the fact that a diode is also regarded as a P-N junction diode. If a suitable positive voltage (forward bias) is applied between the two ends of the PN junction, it can supply free electrons and holes with the extra energy they require to cross the junction as the width of the depletion layer around the PN junction is decreased. See the charged ions in the diagrams of figure 3.10c below.

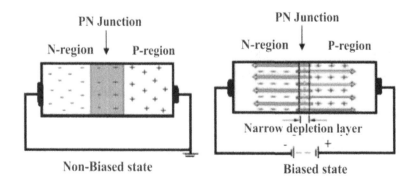

Figure 3.10c: Electrons and Holes movement in Diodes

By applying a negative voltage (reverse bias), free charged ions are being pulled away from the junction resulting in the depletion layer becoming widened, thereby increasing or decreasing the effective resistance of the junction by allowing or blocking current flow through the diode.

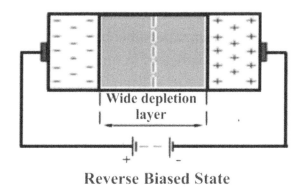

Reverse Biased State

Figure 3.10d: Electrons and Holes movement in Diodes

The depletion layer widens with an increase in the application of a reverse voltage and narrows with an increase in the application of a forward voltage. This is due to the differences in the electrical properties on the two sides of the PN junction resulting in physical changes taking place.

Diodes are manufactured in a range of voltage and current ratings and care must be taken when choosing a diode for a certain application or when applying heat during soldering. The following are rated features;

- Peak inverse voltage which is the maximum allowable Reverse operating voltage that can be applied across the diode without reverse breakdown and damage occurring to the device.
- Maximum Forward Current which is the *maximum forward current* allowed to flow through the device. When the diode is conducting in the forward bias condition, it has a very small "ON" resistance across the P-N junction and therefore, power is dissipated across this junction (according to **Ohm's Law**) in the form of heat. Therefore, exceeding its maximum forward current value will cause more heat to be generated across the junction and the diode will fail due to thermal overload, usually with destructive consequences.

- Total Power Dissipation rating which is the maximum possible power dissipation of the diode when it is forward biased (conducting). When current flows through the signal diode, the biasing of the P-N junction is not perfect and offers some resistance to the flow of current resulting in power being dissipated (lost) in the diode in the form of heat.
- Maximum Operating Temperature rating actually relates to the *Junction Temperature* of the diode and maximum power dissipation. It is the maximum temperature allowable before the structure of the diode deteriorates and is expressed in units of degrees centigrade per Watt, ($^{\circ}$C/W).

Power diodes provide uncontrolled rectification of power and are used in applications such as battery charging circuits and DC power supplies as well as AC rectifiers and inverters. Power diodes are designed to have a forward "ON" resistance of fractions of an Ohm while their reverse blocking resistance is in the mega-Ohms range.

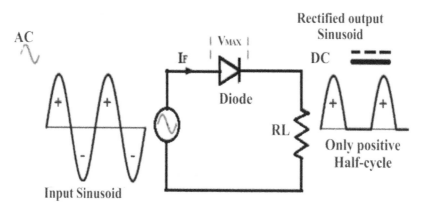

Figure 3.10e: Power diode as a rectifier

If an alternating voltage is applied across a power diode, during the positive half- cycle the diode will conduct, passing current and during the negative half cycle the diode will not conduct blocking the flow of current. Therefore, conduction through the power diode only occurs during the positive half-cycle and is unidirectional i.e. DC. This is known as rectification.

Power diodes can be used individually like in the diagram above or connected together to produce a variety of rectifier circuits such as "Half-Wave", "Full-Wave" or as "Bridge Rectifiers". Each type of rectifier circuit can be classified as uncontrolled, half-controlled or fully controlled. An uncontrolled rectifier circuit is implemented using only power diodes; a fully controlled rectifier circuit is implemented using thyristors (SCRs) while a half controlled rectifier is a mixture of both diodes and thyristors.

Half Wave Rectification

A rectifier is a circuit which converts an Alternating Current (AC) input power into a Direct Current (DC) output power as is common in AC/DC adapters. The input power supply may be either a single-phase or a multi-phase supply. The most simple configuration type among all the rectifier circuits is that of the Half-Wave Rectifier.

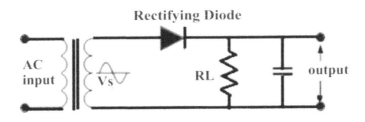

Figure 3.10f: Diode as a Half-wave Rectifier

The power diode in a half-wave rectifier circuit passes just one half of each complete sine wave of the AC supply in order to convert it into a DC supply. That is where this type of circuit derived its name.

During each "positive" half-cycle of the AC sine wave, the diode is forward-biased as the anode is positive with respect to the cathode resulting in current flowing through the diode. During the "negative" half cycle, the diode goes into blocking mode.

When rectification provides a (DC) power supply from an alternating (AC) source as found in most power supply units of consumer electronics, the amount of ripple voltage can be further reduced by using high capacity capacitors to smoothen the resultant output waveform. Cost and size limitations are factored into the types of smoothing capacitors used. For a given capacitor value, a greater load current will discharge the capacitor more quickly, thereby increasing the ripples output.

For a single-phase, half-wave rectifier circuit using a power diode, it is not very practical to try and reduce the ripple voltage by capacitor smoothing alone. "Full-wave Rectification" is recommended.

The Full Wave Rectifier

Like the half wave circuit, a Full Wave Rectifier Circuit produces an output voltage or current which is purely DC. Full wave rectifiers have some advantages over the half wave rectifier circuit. The average DC output voltage is higher than that of half wave rectifier and the output of the full wave rectifier also has much less ripple than that of the half wave rectifier, producing a smoother output waveform.

Two diodes are used in a Full Wave Rectifier circuit, one for each half of the cycle. A multiple winding transformer with a common centre-tapped connection is used by splitting the secondary winding equally into two halves. Each diode in this design conducts in turn when its anode terminal is positive with respect to the transformer centre point "C", producing a d.c linear output during both half-cycles that is twice that of the half wave rectifier. See the circuit design image below;

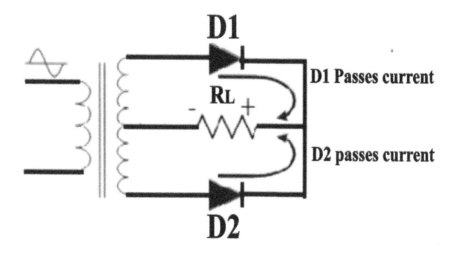

Figure 3.10g: Diode as a Full-wave Rectifier

The Diode Full Wave Bridge Rectifier

There is another kind of diode full wave rectification design with a bridge connection which is common in most electronic devices' power supply units. It is another type of circuit that produces the same output waveform as the full wave rectifier circuit. This type of single-phase rectifier uses four individual rectifying diodes connected in a closed loop "bridge" configuration to produce the desired DC output.

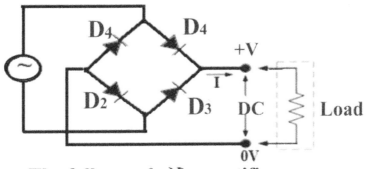

The full wave bridge rectifier

Figure 3.10h: The Full-wave Bridge Rectifier

The four diodes labelled D1 to D4 in figure 3.10h are arranged in "series pairs" with only two diodes conducting current during each half-cycle. During the positive half-cycle of the supply, diodes D1 and D2 conduct in series while diodes D3 and D4 are reverse-biased and the current flows through the load. During the negative half-cycle of the supply, diodes D3 and D4 conduct in series, but diodes D1 and D2 switch "OFF" as they are now reverse- biased. The current flowing through the load is in the same direction as before. This design is found easily in DC adapters like the travel charging adapters (chargers) of mobile phones. It is important for technicians to understand this circuit. See what happens in each half-cycle in the diagrams below.

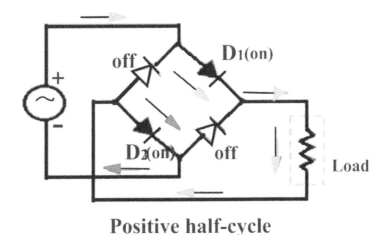

Positive half-cycle

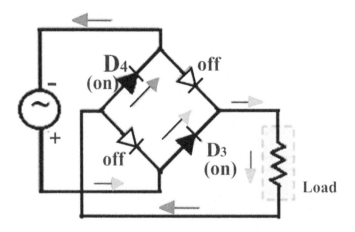

Negative half-cycle

We can also increase the average DC output level even higher by connecting a suitable smoothing capacitor across the output of the bridge circuit as shown below;

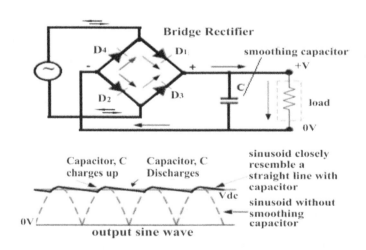

Fig. 3.10i: Diode Full-wave Bridge Rectifier with smoothing capacitor

The objective of rectification is to have a signal current output that travels through conductors in a straight line. The smoothing capacitors converts the full-wave rippled output of the rectifier into a smooth DC output voltage. Generally, for DC power supply circuits, the smoothing capacitor is usually an Aluminium electrolytic type which has a capacitance value of 100uF or more with repeated DC voltage pulses from the rectifier charging up the capacitor to peak voltage.

If the capacitance value is too low, the capacitor will have little effect on the output waveform. But if the smoothing capacitor is sufficiently large enough (parallel capacitors can be used) and the load current is not too large, the output voltage will almost be as smooth as a pure DC voltage.

Light Emitting Diode

A "Light Emitting Diode" or LED is a type of P-N junction diode, specially made from a very thin layer of heavily doped semiconductor material. Therefore, when operated in a forward-biased direction Light Emitting Diodes convert electrical energy into light energy.

In the forward-biased state, electrons from the semiconductor's conduction band recombine with holes from the valence band releasing enough energy to produce photons which emit a single colour spectrum of light. Because of this thin layer, a reasonable number of these photons can leave the junction and radiate away producing a coloured-light output. Thus, the actual colour of a light emitting diode is determined by the wavelength of the light emitted, which in turn is determined by the actual semiconductor compound used in forming the PN junction during manufacture.

The light emitting diodes produces light of low heat radiation which is different compared to the heat generated by incandescent lamps which generate large amounts of heat when illuminated. They are therefore more energy efficient than the normal light bulb. Their generated energy radiates away within the visible light spectrum. They are usually small, durable and provide much longer lamp life. LEDs find application mostly as indicators as found in the old phones' keypads, LCD screen lighting, smartphones and tablets notification lights (charging, flash LEDs) and dashboard of cars etcetera. They are usually connected in the forward bias with a limiting resistor to control the amount of current flowing to the diode.

Zener Diodes

Zener diodes are widely used as voltage reference diodes for making simple voltage regulator circuits in electronic circuits. They are used mainly as power supply regulators or to provide stable reference voltages in the circuit. They can also be used to remove peaks in waveforms that may not be required or to remove spikes that may damage a circuit or cause it to overload.

Figure 3.10i: Zener Diode symbol

Zener diodes function just like an ordinary diode in the forward-bias direction. However in the reverse-biased direction their operation is rather different. For very low voltages, like a normal diode they do not conduct at all. But once a high voltage level is attained, the diode "breaks-down" allowing current to flow. They then maintain a constant voltage regardless of the current carried. You will find Zener diodes in the charging circuits of mobile smartphones and tablets.

Transistors

Transistors are three-terminal active devices made from different semiconductor materials that can act as either an insulator or a conductor by the application of a small signal voltage. Transistors are semiconductor devices used to amplify or switch electronic signals and electrical power. Transistors' native ability to change between states (insulator or conductor) enables them to act as "switches" (in digital electronics) or "amplifiers" (in analogue electronics).

Transistors are the foundation for the digital revolution because without transistors, the technological products used daily like smartphones or tablets and computers would have retained very large form factors which would have been impracticable as mobiles or maybe not mmanufactured at all.

Transistors were initially made from the element germanium. Pure germanium was known to be a good insulator. But adding impurities (a process called doping) changed the germanium into a weak conductor, or semiconductor. This we have discussed earlier.

Doped germanium is used to create transistors in a configuration of either P-N-P or N-P-N by connecting two layers back to back. The point of contact was called a junction. With an electrical current applied to the center layer (called the base), electrons will move from the N-type side to the P-type side. A small initial trickle current acts as a switch that allows much larger current to flow. In an electric circuit, this means that transistors are acting as both a switch and an amplifier.

When we studied diodes in the previous section, we saw that simple diodes are made from two pieces of semiconductor materials, either silicon or germanium to form a simple P-N junction.

If two individual signal diodes are joined together back-to-back, this will give us two P-N junctions connected together in series that share a common P or N terminal. The fusion of these two diodes produces a three-layer, two-junction, three-terminal device forming the basis of a Bipolar Junction Transistor, or BJT for short.

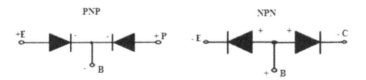

Two Diode Analogy

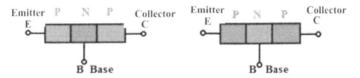

Physical Construction of Transistors

Fig. 3.11a

In electronic circuits, the circuit symbols are as shown in fig.6.11b;

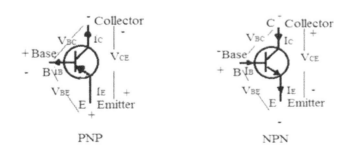

Figure 3.11b: Schematic Symbols and Representation of Transistors

The structure of a transistor is such that they have two P-N junctions with a narrow base region between the two outlying areas for the collector and emitter.

During normal operation, the base-emitter junction is forward-biased while the base-collector junction is reverse-biased. When current flows through the base- emitter junction, current that is larger and proportional to the base current also flows in the collector circuit. Take for instance an NPN transistor as shown below in fig. 3.11c;

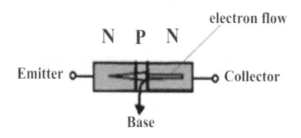

Figure 3.11c: NPN Transistor

The emitter in the n-p-n device is made of n-type material and the majority carriers in the emitter are electrons. When the base-emitter junction is forward-biased, the electrons move from the n-type region towards the p-type region and the holes move towards the n-type region. When they reach each other they combine enabling current to flow across the junction. When the junction is reverse-biased, the holes and electrons move away from one another resulting in a depletion region between the two areas with no current flowing.

When current flows between the base and emitter, electrons leave the emitter and flow into the base. Normally, the electrons would combine when they reach this area. However, the doping level in this region is very low and the base is also very thin. This means that most of the electrons are able to travel across this region without recombining with the holes. As a result, the electrons migrate towards the collector, because they are attracted by the positive potential there. This is how electrons are able to flow across a reverse-biased junction with ease, causing current to flow in the collector circuit.

It has been discovered that the collector current is significantly higher than the base current, and because the proportion of electrons combining with holes remains the same, the collector current is always proportional to the base current.

In other words varying the base current varies the collector current. The ratio of the base to collector current is given by the Greek symbol β - beta which represents the Current Gain. Typically the ratio β can be between 50 and 500 for a small signal transistor. This means that collector current will be between 50 and 500 times the base current. This is current amplification.

Transistors are connected within the PCB in three possible ways with one terminal being "common" to both the input and output. They are;

- Common Base Configuration (Transistor has Voltage Gain but no Current Gain).

- Common Emitter Configuration (Transistor has both Current and Voltage Gain).

- Common Collector Configuration (Transistor has Current Gain but no Voltage Gain).

The common emitter configuration is the most commonly used connection for transistors in digital electronics circuits. We shall not go into more details on these configurations. However, you can do further research and readings about transistors on your own.

Besides functioning as amplifiers as explained above, transistors can also be used in DC circuits to implement "ON / OFF" solid state switching for DC outputs.

Here is how;

How Transistors Function as a Switch

The output from a transistor is usually taken from the collector. The collector current as we saw in the previous explanation is usually a multiple of that of the base current and the ratio of collector current to base current is its current gain. Therefore, since the collector current varies with the base current, a transistor can be used as a current-controlled switch between its cut-off state (OFF) and saturation (ON). The controlled current is the collector current while the controlling current (controller) is the base current.

Since we are talking about a switch, let us create a simple lighting circuit controlled by an ON-OFF switch;

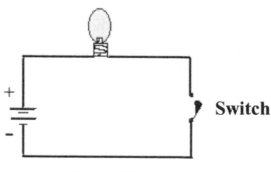

Figure 3.12a

In the diagram above the switch is open therefore, no current flows through the bulb to light it up. Assuming we replace the mechanical switch above with a transistor (NPN or PNP) to control the flow of electrons through the lamp. The controlled current is the collector current and so it must be connected in such a way that the current passes through the transistor between collector and emitter. Therefore the current that passes through and lights the bulb must be the collector current.

Study the diagram in fig. 3.12b;

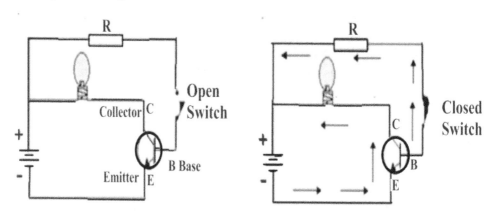

Figure 3.12b

A switch between the base and collector wires of the transistor will supply the base of the transistor with the needed base current to ensure the transistor does not remain in a cut-off state. In the open switch configuration above, the base wire of the transistor is not connected to any source so there will be no base current flow; therefore the transistor will be OFF. But when the switch is closed electrons will be able to flow from the emitter to the base of the transistor, pass through the switch up to the right side of the lamp, back to the positive side of the battery.

This base current will enable a much larger flow of electrons from the emitter to the collector, thus lighting up the lamp. The transistor is said to be saturated at this point which is equivalent to being ON.

In conclusion, any sufficient source of DC current could be used to turn the transistor ON. The transistor in this case was not only functioning as a switch, but as a proper amplifier by using a relatively low power signal to control a larger amount of power. Although the lighting of the bulb is as a result of energy from the battery, any small power source connected to the base of the transistor can serve to control the battery's ability to power up the bulb.

Integrated Circuits, ICs

"An integrated circuit (also referred to as an IC, a chip, or a microchip) is a set of electronic circuits on one small plate ("chip") of semiconductor material, normally silicon. Any circuit in which all or some of the circuit elements are inseparably associated and electrically interconnected so that it is considered to be indivisible for the purposes of construction and commerce is an Integrated Circuit" [14]. I like this definition above from Wikipedia. It properly captures the concept and description of an IC.

The design of ICs is such that they are lightweight, small – as small as a thumbnail. They are constructed to be energy efficient, made up of several billions of transistors and other discrete electronic components in a single chip. Integrated circuits are used in almost all electronic equipment today and have revolutionized the world of electronics. Computers, mobile smartphones, tablets and other digital consumer appliances are now inextricable parts of the structure of modern societies made possible by the low cost of and use of integrated circuits in their PCBs. Integrated circuits can be classified into;

- Analog
- Digital and
- Mixed signal (both analog and digital on the same chip).

Analog ICs includes sensors, power management circuits, and operational amplifiers. They operate by processing sinusoidal analog signals and perform functions like amplification, active filtering, demodulation, and signal-mixing. With Analog ICs, circuit designers do not have to be bordered about designing a difficult analog circuit from start to finish since analog circuits are expertly designed and sold off the shelf.

Digital integrated circuit packages can contain anywhere from one to millions of logic gates, flip-flops, multiplexers, and other circuits in thumbnail sized material.

Because of the small size of these circuits, their properties include high speed, low power dissipation, and reduced manufacturing cost contrasted with circuit-board-level integration.

Digital ICs such as microprocessors, DSPs, and microcontrollers, operate using binary mathematics to process "1s" and "0s" signals.
ICs can also *"combine analog and digital circuits on a single chip to create functions such as A/D (Analog-to-Digital) converters and D/A (Digital-to-Analog) converters. Such mixed-signal circuits' offer smaller size and lower cost, but must carefully account for signal interference."* [15].

IC Packaging has evolved over the years. The various packages are listed below. But for the purposes of our interest in this study in mobile phones' IC chips, we shall only discuss further on the BGA chips package.

The following are the various naming schemes for IC packages in use at various times in the history of ICs;

- *Dual in Line (DIP) as seen in earlier home electronics gadgets.*
- *Pin Grid Array (PGA) as seen in computer Microprocessors.*
- *Leadless Chip Carrier (LCC) as seen in computer Microprocessors also called "pin-less chip" in local parlance.*
- *Plastic Quad Flat Pack (PQFP).*
- *Thin Small Outline Pack (TSOP).*
- *Ball Grid Array (BGA) or the Flip-Chip Ball Grid Array (FCBGA) as seen in mobile phone PCBs.* [16]

Surface Mount Technology (SMT) and Ball Grid Arrays (BGA)

A Ball Grid Array (BGA) package is a form of surface mount technology, or SMT package that is being used increasingly for integrated circuits. Necessity they say is the mother of invention. Integrated circuits with large number of pins necessitated that a more robust and convenient package be developed. As more and more components were being packed into IC chips, the number of pins also increased with some integrated circuits having more than 100 pins. The BGA design was therefore developed to improve on the arrangement and surface area space for IC mounting. The BGA uses the underside of the package, where there is a considerable surface area for the connections. The pins are placed in a matrix grid pattern on the under-surface of the chip carrier which is the reason it is called Ball Grid Array. The "Ball"(s) is solder ball joints.

Rather than using pins to provide the connectivity, pads with balls of solder are used as the method of connection.

On the printed circuit board, PCB, on which the BGA device is to be fitted, there is a matching set of copper pads to provide the required connectivity.

BGA Chips

Figure 3.13

Sensors, Transducers and Automation

Every electronic system or circuit is designed to perform a specific function. This means that a circuit, sub-circuit or whole system unit is built to do something specific. In order for circuits to achieve their purpose, they must be capable of sensing an input of any kind. For instance, for a device to power ON or OFF it must sense an input signal from a source that commands the system to either ON or OFF. Likewise if the device should produce an output on the display or screen like in mobile smartphones, a signal must activate that output.

Electrical Transducers are used for converting one form of energy into energy of another kind. For instance, a microphone in a mobile device (input device) converts sound waves (voice) into electrical signals for the amplifier to amplify (a process), and a loudspeaker (output device) converts these electrical signals back into sound waves.

Sensors on the other hand sense a wide range of different energy forms such as movement, electrical signals, radiant energy, thermal or magnetic energy etc. They "sense" any physical change in some Characteristic of a device that changes in response to some excitation. The type of input or output transducer used in a system will depend on the type of signal or process being "Sensed" or "Controlled".

Sensors are input-type transducers which produces a voltage or signal output response that is proportional to the change in the quantity being measured. The type or amount of the output signal depends on the type of sensor being used. There are sensors which function only when a signal like current or voltage is applied to it from an external source.

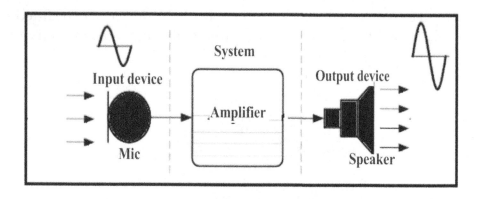

Figure 3.14: Sample sound system transducers

Such applied signals will alter the internal properties of the sensor thereby making it to produce an output response.

However, other types of sensors do not need any external signal source. Rather, physical, environmental or natural stimuli affect their behavior and make them to generate an electric signal in response to such external stimulus. A photo-diode for example lights up as a result of light energy stimuli. You find these kinds of diode on the LCD of phone screens where the level of light on the screen modulates with exposure to light. Proximity sensors are built into smartphones which react when it detects the presence of nearby objects without physical contact of any sort. It is usually implemented based on the target object to be sensed. So the proximity sensor could be electromagnetic as found in infrared sensors on the front of mobile phones; capacitive, inductive or photoelectric sensors if the target object is plastic or a metal object respectively. These kinds of sensors change their physical properties, such as resistance, capacitance or inductance etcetera, when they sense an external stimulus.

The output produced by any of the various types of these sensors can either be analogue or digital. If Digital, they produce a discrete output represented as binary digits such as a logic level "0" or a logic level "1". Analogue Sensors however, measure physical quantities such as Temperature, Speed, Pressure, Displacement (like accelerometers in smartphones which help to maintain image orientation in an upright position by detecting the device's position), and Strain etc. They produce a sinusoidal (AC) output signal or voltage which is usually proportional to the quantity being measured, very small in value ranging from a few micro-volts to several milli-volts (mV). They are usually subjected to the process of amplification and then converted into digital signals for further processing in the micro-controller systems using analogue-to-digital converters (AD/DA converters).

Finally, it is clear that Sensors and transducers aid in automating processes and system functions. To fix mobile smartphones and tablets, you need to recognize their in-built features, the sensors controlling such features and how they work in order to be effective in problem-solving.

Smartphones Circuit Analysis

Now that you have read this chapter up to this second section, Circuit Analysis, it is important to add to your skill set, the application of this basic electronics knowledge in analyzing circuits in order to fix faults in PCBs. In this section, some general methods for analysis of electrical circuits will be taught. The job of a technician often entails "troubleshooting", a process for locating and correcting a problem in malfunctioning circuits. Troubleshooting is a demanding and rewarding effort which requires;

- A thorough understanding of the basic concepts of the technology;
- The ability to mentally formulate assumptions and explanations of an effect;
- The ability to critically evaluate the outcome of various assumptions based on the possibility of one particular cause over another and;
- A high sense of creativity in applying a solution to rectify the problem.

It is pertinent to note that while it takes some years of experience to master the art of troubleshooting, it is also very important that a technician can easily and intuitively understand how a faulty component could affect circuits in different designs.
This necessitated the writing of this chapter with all the concepts, principles and component information.

Components Failure Analysis and Analyzing Basic Circuit Diagrams

There are a number of tools used for analyzing very small electrical/electronic circuits. For instance when faced with a small electrical/electronic circuit, a good technician should do any or all of the following among other physical checks and actions;

- Identify resistor combinations to ascertain if they are either series or parallel connections.
- Identify voltage or current sources so that you can apply Thevenin or Norton theorems' equivalent.
- Identify embedded voltage dividers in the circuit.

- Identify electrical continuities, links between components tracing a map of the circuit.
- Identify and isolate the affected final sub-circuit that demands attention and repair.

To further establish the causes of failure, there are two general methods used:

- The method of analyzing node voltages and
- The loop equation method

Before we continue, let us review and explain some current and voltage laws you may or may not have seen while reading this chapter. They are;

- Kirchhoff's Circuit Laws (Current and Voltage laws)
- Ohm's laws (We have treated Ohm's law earlier)
- Thevenin's Theorem
- Norton's Theorem

Kirchhoff's circuit laws are two equalities that define the current and voltage in the lumped element model of electrical circuits. They were first described in 1845 by German physicist Gustav Kirchhoff and widely used in electrical engineering, called Kirchhoff's laws. Kirchhoff's current law combined with Ohm's Law is used in nodal analysis.

Kirchhoff's first law states that:

"At any node (junction) in an electrical circuit, the sum of currents flowing into that node is equal to the sum of currents flowing out of that node"

Or equivalently;

"The algebraic sum of currents in a network of conductors meeting at a point is zero."

This Kirchhoff's current law above is represented mathematically as;

$$\sum_{K=1}^{n} I_k = 0$$

Where n is the total number of branches with currents flowing towards or away from the node and I = current.

Kirchhoff's voltage law (KVL) also called Kirchhoff's second law states that;

"The sum of all the voltages around a loop is equal to zero."

The principle of conservation of energy implies that the directed sum of the electrical voltage around any closed network is zero, or:

"The sum of the EMFs (Electromotive Force) in any closed loop is equivalent to the sum of the potential drops in that loop" or:

"The algebraic sum of the products of the resistances of the conductors and the currents in them (remember V= I x R) in a closed loop is equal to the total EMF available in that loop" represented mathematically as;

$$\sum_{K=1}^{n} V_k = 0$$

Thevenin's Theorem on the other hand states that any combination of batteries and resistances with two terminals can be replaced by a single voltage source "e" and a single series resistor "r". The value of e is the open circuit voltage at the terminals, and the value of r is e divided by the current, i with the terminals short circuited.

While **Norton's Theorem** states that *"any collection of batteries and resistances with two terminals is electrically equivalent to an ideal current source, i in parallel with a single resistor, r."*

The value of r is the same as that in the Thevenin equivalent and the current i can be found by dividing the open circuit voltage by r.

Analyzing Node Voltages

Assuming we have a simple circuit as shown below;

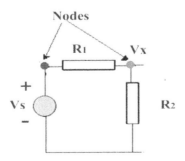

To begin analyzing this circuit, we write the KCL equations for the nodes in the circuit. The equations are written in terms of **node** voltages (although the Current Law is used, the variables are in voltages).

The circuit above is a voltage divider circuit. Two nodes exist in the circuit marked "blue" color and "red" color respectively. Each **node** is different from the other.

I.   The voltage at the blue **node** is equal to the voltage at the source, if Vs - the source voltage – is known (for instance a 12V battery source).

II. The voltage at the red **node** can only be found through calculation.

Consequently, let us assume that; since there is only one node with unknown voltage, there's going to be one equation and the equation we need to write is KCL at the node with the unknown voltage!

i.   First, define the unknown voltage as **Vx**. Define the two currents flowing to and from the nodes (see figure below).

ii. Then we write KCL (Kirchhoff's Current Law) at the node where Vx appears.

iii. Finally, we solve whatever equation results from writing KCL.

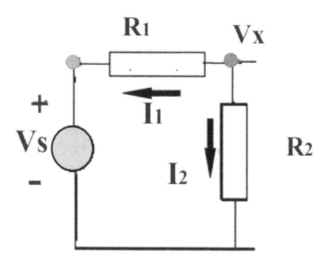

Then, according to KCL;

$I_1 + I_2 = 0$ since both currents are leaving the red node.

To calculate the value for I_1 and I_2, we apply Ohm's law;

V = IR and so **I = V/R**

Where V_S = Source voltage and V_X = Unknown voltage

$$I_1 = (V_X - V_S) / R_1$$
$$I_2 = (V_X - 0) / R_2$$

In both cases the voltage across the resistor causing the current to flow in the indicated direction is:

= Voltage at the node V_X - Voltage across each of the other resistor end.

Note that one end of R_2 is connected to ground, so it records a zero voltage.

Explanation: To understand how each current is calculated, and the exact formula for the current.

The current, I, through a resistor, R, connected to a node is:

$$I = \frac{(\text{Voltage at the node - Voltage at the other resistor end})}{R}$$

Since:
$$I_1 = (V_X - V_S) / R_1 \text{ and}$$
$$I_2 = (V_X - 0) / R_2$$

We can write the complete KCL equation thus; $Ia + Ib = 0$.

So, we have: $[(V_X - V_S) / R_1] + [(V_X - 0) / R_2] = 0$

Now, remember the algorithm for using node voltages.
Solve whatever equation results from writing KCL.

The result is:

$$V_X = V_S * \frac{R_1}{(R_1 + R_2)}$$

The simultaneous equation above and the result can at best be said to be simplistic compared to the numerous complex circuits encountered in the real world in consumer electronics products.

In this book, there is no motivation or persuasion to bore the reader with complex mathematical equations. It is just to spur your mind to relate with the reality of problem resolutions through knowledge which is available and acquired in regular educational institutions.

There is no denying the fact that most people tend to see electronics and its wonders as some form of magic at work.

As a technician, aspiring technician or engineer, graduate technician or engineer; whatever category of reader you might be; you have been challenged. This chapter had me trying to review as much information as possible; to transfer enough perspective and background information as possible; to motivate any reader to become the best kind of technical support provider and my hope is that the reader has gained enough information for the task ahead or has been challenged enough to seek further knowledge and clarifications from several knowledge sources that abound. Before we wrap up this chapter, let us see a few samples of mobile phones' final sub-circuits in reality.

Mobile Phone Battery Charging System

The charging adapter is usually called a "charger" by both users and technicians alike. In reality, it is just an Analog-to-Digital converter used to supply direct current (D.C) input to the battery charging circuit (the actual charger) in the motherboard of the mobile device. They come as single-pin type or multi-pin type.

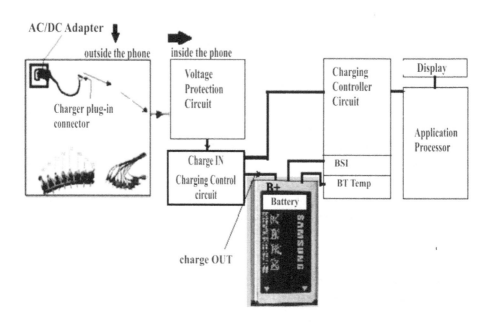

Figure 3.15a: The charging system

Battery charger technologies vary, from the simple trickle-charge, timer-based ones to the intelligent, fast, pulse, inductive, USB based chargers. Others are solar chargers, wireless chargers and motion powered chargers.

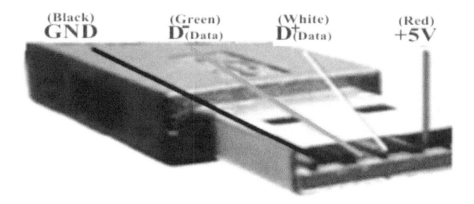

Figure 3.15b: USB Pinout diagram

Most chargers manufactured in recent times are USB based systems. From the image above, the USB plug consists of four wires of different colors. The green and white wires are for data while the red and black are for positive and negative polarity charging current. This should aid in tracing the circuit. Follow the steps in a later section "Repairing Faulty Charging Circuits" in chapter 7.

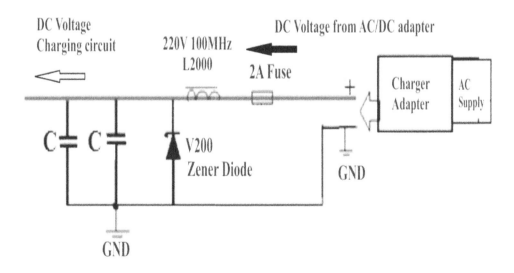

Figure 3.15c: Sample charging circuit A

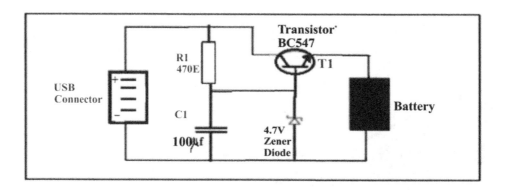

Figure 3.15d: Sample charging circuit B

How the Circuit Functions: Home electrical power systems supply between 110V AC in some countries and 220-240V AC in other countries. This energy supply in socket outlets is tapped by charger adapters which converts the AC voltage to a desired DC voltage between 5 to 5.5 volts DC. Electronic devices utilize only DC voltage and current, not AC. The DC voltage outputs of chargers are rectified "impure" DC voltages which are fed as input to the phone through the charger pins that connects to the phone's charging connector.

Mobile phone's charging circuit is usually composed of a Fuse, Inductor, Diodes (usually a Zener diode voltage regulator) and filtering Capacitors. The protection elements in this section of the circuit are the fuse and the Zener diode. Before the DC voltage reaches the charging voltage control circuits, this protection circuit controls and maintains the voltage at a fixed rating determined by the Zener diode.

Assuming the desired amount of DC voltage is only 5.0 volts, when the incoming voltage exceeds 5.0V DC the diode will then cut off or become shorted, current will flow to ground and the fuse will cut-out totally disconnecting the voltage line. The inductor's role is to filter unwanted voltage saturation by rejecting abnormal voltage modulation.

At the Charger Voltage Control Circuit, the DC voltage and current is then stabilized, regulated and other voltage purification process is carried out before it is fed to the battery. All the while, the charging process is monitored by a Charging Control Circuit which shares the information with either the Analog baseband
CPU or the application processor - depending on the type of phone - to start or stop the charging process. This is part of the Power Management circuit within the POWER IC (Universal Energy Manager, UEM or other chip nomenclature depending on the manufacturer).

What happens is that a signal from the voltage control circuit sends data to the charging control circuit.

This data informs the charging control circuit that a charger voltage is being sensed. The charging control circuit will then analyze and convert that data into digital signal before transmitting it to the Application processor.

Smartphone Audio circuits

Audio codec circuit controls sound signals in a mobile device. It is a kind of audio amplifier, an audio mixer or a sound booster. During transmission and reception of phone calls, voice message signal is converted into radio frequency signal while incoming radio frequency signal is converted into sound signals. Its circuit therefore, functions for both microphones and speakers of the mobile device as the microphone's sound signal is being amplified and then converted to radio frequency before transmission to the network. The reverse happens for the speaker. Below is a typical block diagram of audio interfaces interconnection with the audio codec circuit.

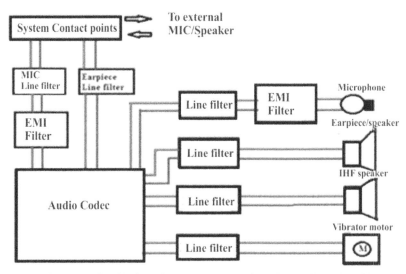

Block diagram of audio interfaces interconnection with audio codec chip

Figure 3.16a

The block diagrams and the following sample schematic circuit diagrams for mobile phone's microphone, speaker, ringer and vibrator circuits are for the reader to appreciate the interconnections between these components' sub-circuits on the PCB; the various relationships and interdependencies between them and their controlling chips. This will serve as an aid during troubleshooting, in deciding where the fault lies with a non-functional component - which IC requires reflow soldering when the component and its associated discrete electronic components are determined to be in good condition, but fail to function in the system - and also possible track trace paths.

From the audio block diagram above, the line filters are filtering capacitors for noise (noise is an analog signal (AC), so it is filtered through capacitors to ground) reduction and of course you will find resistors and inductors too. The earpiece circuit below is being filtered by an inductor coil to reduce sound saturation caused by any radio frequency interruption. It is expected that your study of discrete electronic components should become handy during troubleshooting and fault correction.

Note: *The circuits are not exactly as shown in all mobile smartphones and tablets in the market. While the concept and underlying technology remains the same, manufacturers and design configurations may change or varies.*

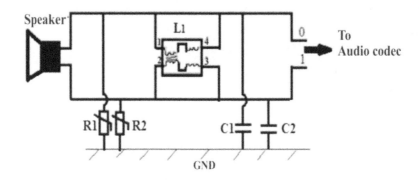

Figure 3.16b: Sample Circuit Diagram for Speakers

Study the audio block diagram above, the Microphone circuit is being protected by an EMI - Filter (Electromagnetic Interference filter) to prevent audio interruptions before the audio codec circuit receives a voice signal. It might or might not be incorporated into a circuit based on the design. The microphone signal is being filtered by two capacitors after being passed-by from an EMI-Filter in order to remove the DC current coming from the EMI-filter.

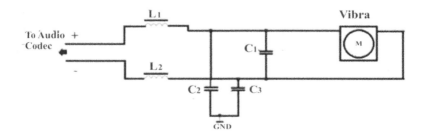

Figure 3.16c: Sample Vibrator circuit
*This is just an illustrative image

SIM Card Circuits

A SIM Card is a Smart Card that can store data for and from a cellular phone. Such data includes network authorization, authentication and encryption; subscriber identification number, personal security keys, user contact lists and stored text messages. It has six contact pads that correspond to six PCB SIM connector pins, although one of the pins has no connection linked to it. They are;

SIM DATA: This is for digital data stored on a SIM memory

SIM Clock: This is for synchronization.

SIM Reset: This is for sending a frequency signal that triggers or reset all synchronization process.

VSIM B+ Supply Voltage: This pin provides the power supply voltage used to activate the SIM circuit.

SIM Ground pin: This pin is for ground line voltage.

One of the pins is not connected (NC).

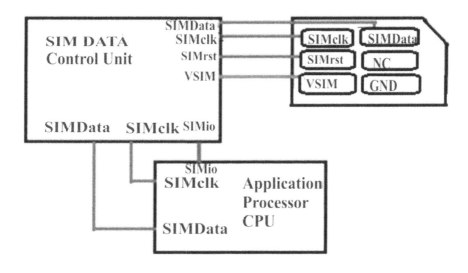

Figure 3.17: Block diagram of SIM Circuitry

From the pictorial image in fig. 3.17, it is easier to match the pin configurations of the SIM connector when fixing a SIM fault. This helps to trace the tracks to reference discrete components. For instance, looking at the block diagram above, one can confirm the reference voltage supply to the SIM by taking measurement between VSIM and GND pins. Without SIM inserted, as soon as the phone is switched ON, the BSI line grounded by a resistor, all SIM interfaces rises first to 3V and then 5V. If you are not getting any of either voltage at those pins, then the SIM control unit (usually a separate glass chip controller in some phones or integrated into the microprocessor in others) could be the cause. The solder balls underneath either of the ICs can have disconnected and reflow soldering used to correct the fault in most cases.

Touchscreen Systems

Touchscreens are field replaceable units; they are usually not repaired but replaced. It might help to have just a basic understanding of what they are like.

They are a separate transparent glass or screen overlay on mobile device LCDs that are used to provide keyboard or User-Command Controlled input to the system through simple or multi-touch gestures using one or more fingers or a pen/stylus. With touchscreens in mobile devices, users interact directly with the LCD display output rather than using keyboard buttons. This technology has become the predominant input system for smartphones and tablets.

Two types of touchscreens have been implemented in mobile phones so far: The Resistive type and The Capacitive type touchscreens.

Resistive Touchscreens

Resistive Touchscreen technologies are analog, require moving parts and electrical resistance to sense touch while Capacitive Touchscreen technology is digital, require solid state components and the presence of electrical capacitance to sense touch.

The image in fig. 3.17a illustrates the concept of resistive touchscreens. The design is such that two electrically conductive layers bend to touch one another, with the panel layers calculating the value of resistance that produces changes in current through them at the point touched.

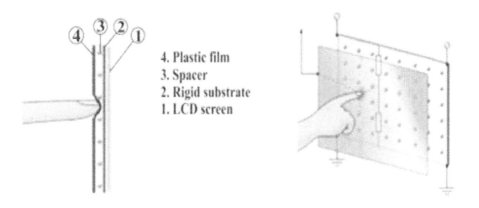

4. Plastic film
3. Spacer
2. Rigid substrate
1. LCD screen

Fig. 3.17a: Resistive Touchscreen illustration

Advantages: They are durable, inexpensive, and respond to other sources of touch than the finger.

Disadvantages: They are single-touch and therefore cannot perform multi-touch functions. Low visual clarity is also a drawback.

Capacitive Touchscreens

Capacitive touchscreens are the predominant digitizers in use today and can either be surface types or projective types. They are the industry standard at the moment as most mobile devices come equipped with capacitive touchscreens. Surface-type capacitive touchscreens have sensors embedded at the corners and a thin evenly distributed film across the surface whereas the projective capacitive type uses a grid of rows and columns with a separate chip used for sensing touch. Both types are designed based on the conductive property of the human skin.

Advantages: Better screen clarity, higher sensitivity to touch and multi touch capabilities are some of the main advantages.

Disadvantages: They are susceptible to electrical noise, more expensive, consume more processing power, and only limited to touch from conductive surfaces.

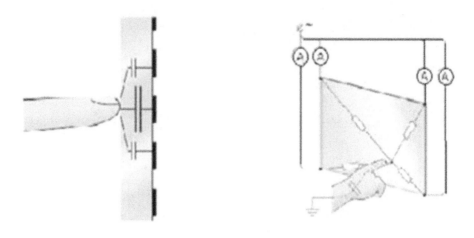

Fig. 3.17b: Capacitive Touchscreen Illustration

Keypad Systems

It is also important to understand at basic level how the matrix keypad system works. This will be of immense benefit for troubleshooting keypad related faults.

How Basic Standard 12 Button Keypad Matrix Works

Currently, keypad matrix functions are implemented with software running on the display systems in sync with the digitizer hardware chip. It is important to understand how a device works in order to fix it. Let me briefly explain therefore, how a keypad matrix works.

Given a standard basic mobile phone with a 4x3 keypad, which have the numbers 0-9, * and #, each square with a number or letter on the hex pad is pushed to make contact forming a switch, which connects the horizontal wires (rows) with the vertical wires (columns).

When button '*' is pressed for instance, it will connect COL1 with ROW4, or if button '6' is pressed it will connect COL3 with ROW2.

Description: The keypad matrix is divided into Rows and Columns. They are an interface technique used to interface inputs like the Mobile Phone keypads, PC keyboard keys, and also to control multiple outputs like LEDs.

Figure 6.19a: 3 x 4 Keypad Buttons and Keypad PCB

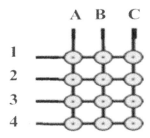

3 x 4 Keypad matrix

Figure 3.19b

The vertical lines are the columns while the horizontal lines are the rows. These rows and columns intersect at 12 points or joints although the columns and the rows are NOT in contact. They are electrically separate but can only be joined together as a switch when the finger presses down the keypad. Then the concave disc contacts merge with the dual concentric gold contacts. The naming scheme for the buttons follow the convention - 'Column: Row' according to their point of intersection. For instance, the top-left button is named A1 and the bottom left is named A4 and so on.

Operation: The matrix is controlled by a microcontroller. For the 12-button 3x4 matrix above, 7 pins of the micro controller will be used. The first 3 pins will be OUTPUTS and will be connected to the COLUMN wires, while the other 4 pins will be INPUTS and will be connected to the ROW wires. The OUTPUTS of the microcontroller IC will NOT be powered simultaneously. The outputs will go 'high' (logic '1') one after the other in cycles. This is repeated many times per second. The microcontroller monitors the inputs for a signal. When all inputs are LOW, the microcontroller will take no action.

But if a user presses button 2B for instance, it connects the matrix column B with row 2. When the "B" output of the Microcontroller goes HIGH, the signal arrives also at the input 2 of the microcontroller, through the pressed (input) button.

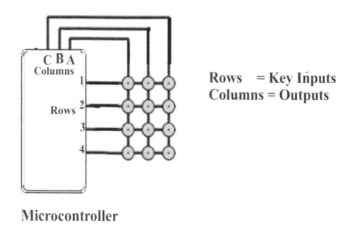

Rows = Key Inputs
Columns = Outputs

Microcontroller

Figure 3.19c

The microcontroller usually loops its outputs and monitors the input lines so that it detects when a specific output like "B" in this case is high, with a corresponding HIGH signal at the input line 2. This means therefore that the input B2 has been pressed.

Multiple buttons pressed simultaneously on a matrix will either produce no output on the display or the first key pressed is displayed. There are situations where the matrix operates normally, but not always. It is for such reasons diodes are introduced in the circuit to stop current from flowing backwards. In mobile devices, the diodes add additional needed functionality of providing keypad lighting by using LEDs (Light Emitting Diodes) in traditional keypads.

Switches

A switch is a device used to direct the flow of electric current across two joints in a circuit. It could be a mechanical, manual operated type or an automatic electronic type of switch. When used at a power supply line-input to a system, they are called power switch-types which are used to switch a device ON or OFF.

There are several applications for switches. However, in all applications they are used for controlling one or more of the various electrical quantities in a circuit such as AC/DC current, resistance, voltage etc.

Primarily a switch is used to 'close' a circuit at a point in the circuit which by design is deliberately kept 'open'. Switches are either completely ON or completely OFF.

In this section, we shall be examining the various manually operated switches with physical buttons for user interface control in mobile devices. They include;

- Power ON/OFF switch
- Side Volume control switches
- Camera ON/OFF switches

Common types of switches used in Mobile devices to control the above listed user interface buttons are;
a. Push button switch-type
b. Toggle switches
c. Joystick switches
d. Variable resistance potentiometer switch-type
e. Digital logic switch-type

How the Push Button Switch-type Works

The push button switch-type has two contact terminals inside with a push bar from the top. When pressed down, the top bar with a dual position spring-load (top and bottom) closes the two terminals and maintains that position while current is passed across its terminals. When pressed again, the spring load releases the top bar and the circuit opens again. If used as a power switch, it controls two states: ON and OFF.

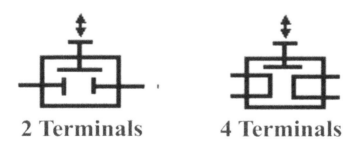

2 Terminals   4 Terminals

Figure 3.20a

How the Toggle Switch-type Works

Toggle switches are actuated by a lever angled in one of two or more positions. The common light switch used in household wiring is an example of a toggle switch. Most toggle switches will come to rest in any of their lever positions, while others have an internal spring mechanism, returning the lever to a certain normal position that allow for what is called "momentary" operation.

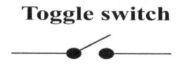

Figure 3.20c

How the Joystick Switch Type Works

Joystick switches are actuated by a lever designed to freely move in more than one axis of motion. The particular way the lever is pushed or how far it is pushed actuates one or more of several switch contact terminals. The direction of the joystick's lever motion required to actuate the contact may be clockwise or anticlockwise. Joystick hand switches were used in earlier versions of smartphones.

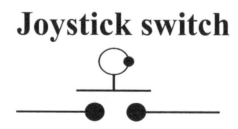

Figure 3.20d

How the Potentiometer Switch Type Works

Potentiometer switches are electronic components that function as variable resistors. The main component within the device is a resistor, illustrated between terminals A and B below. There is a third terminal 'C' that slides along the resistance, selecting a value between the highest and lowest quantity. As the slider moves, the resistance between it and the ends of the resistor change, allowing specific current value to pass.

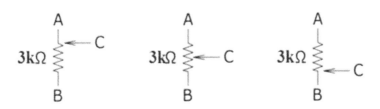

Figure 3.20e: How variable resistors work

In the illustration above, when the movable slider is at the topmost end of the resistor, there will be very little resistance between terminals A and C, with 3KΩ between B and C. In the middle image, the slider is at the center of the resistor, so we'll have 1.5KΩ from terminal C to both A and B. Finally, the moving terminal is at the far end of the resistor, with 3KΩ from A to C, and 0Ω from B to C. Switches based on this design come in various forms and sizes.

Recommended Action

Kindly go through this chapter one more time before delving into the repair procedures in the next chapter. Understanding is important to mastering the repair process.

Chapter 4

Repair Tools and Instrumentation

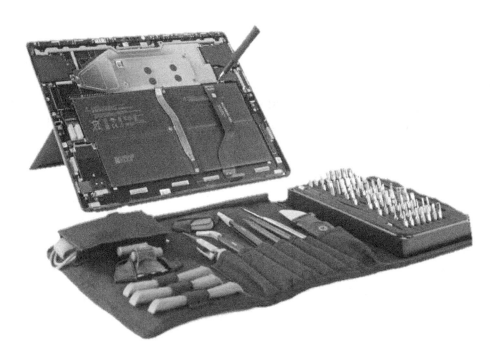

Hardware Repair Tools

Understanding tools and instrumentation is the first thing an entrant to technical support should grasp as it is the key to effectiveness on the job. There is a saying that "a bad workman always blames his tools". So we will start right from here so that you do not become a bad workman.

As a startup technician, have it in mind that there are tools that are very expensive which one might not be able to afford at start-up. Most of the basic tools are cheaper and easy to get and if equipped with the right skill set and knowledge about smartphone repairs as done by this book, the basic tools can generate quickly, enough money to make those big budget purchases. Find the list of tools and equipment with pictures below.

1. Soldering Iron and Soldering Station: Used for Soldering. The standalone Iron on the left is the cheapest tool for beginners if one cannot afford the rework station yet. The challenge is to get the right millimeter tip required. File the tip and use it for practice on dummy electronic boards until mastery is attained. The hot air rework station on the other hand is good for micro-soldering, whereby controlled hot streams of air are channeled to microelectronic components during removal, replacement or rework procedures.

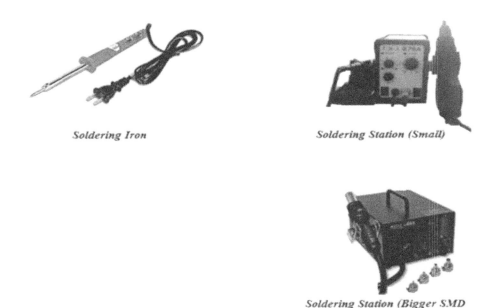

Soldering Iron   Soldering Station (Small)

Soldering Station (Bigger SMD Rework Station)

Figure 4.1: Soldering Iron and Rework Stations

2. Tweezers: Electronic board components are usually tiny and require the use of tweezers to pick them out or place or hold them down during soldering. They are very handy tools during the repair process.

Tweezers

Figure 4.2: Tweezers

3. Soft Brush is used for cleaning the electronic board with Isopropyl Alcohol (IPA)

Figure 4.3: Soft brush

4. Digital Pocket Multi-meter: Basic instrumentation device used for electrical measurements while troubleshooting faults by measuring supply voltage and current values, resistance testing, motherboard wiring continuity checks and so on. There are various types of the product in the market. Below is a simple basic digital meter in fig. 3.4;

Figure 4.4: Digital Multi-meter

5. Nose Cutter for cutting wires

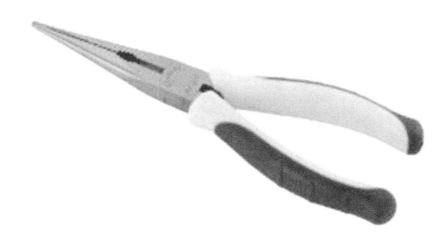

Figure 4.5: Nose Cutter

6. Screwdriver set used for mobile phone disassembly and reassembly by removing and re-tightening the screw nuts in the mobile phone. See image in fig. 3.6;

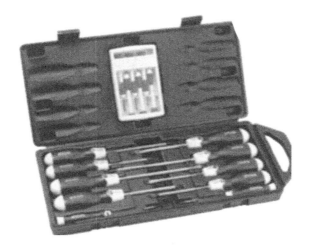

Figure 4.6: Screwdriver set

7. Soldering leads used together with the soldering iron during soldering;

Figure 4.7: Soldering lead

8. P.C.B (Printed Circuit Board) or Motherboard Clamp-Stand or Holder used for fixing the electronic board in place while carrying out repairs on it. It is not mandatory to own one of these but it is helpful.

Figure 4.8: PCB Clamp-Stand/Holder

9. Soldering Fluxes used during the soldering process for effective heat transfer and to prevent oxidation. They come in liquid and paste forms.

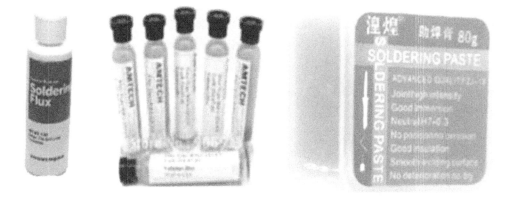

Figure 4.9: Soldering pastes

10. Magnifying Glass and Lamp are used to magnify the electronic board's view in order to see the tiny components properly. For higher precisions of vision, when affordable a microscope is necessary for the job.

Magnifying Lamp   **Magnifying Glass**

Figure 4.10: Magnifying tools

11. Mobile Phone Casing Openers used for slicing open conjoined front and back fascia of mobile phones. They come in different forms and

shapes and a technician can also improvise a means for safe disassembly.

Figure 4.11: Casing openers

12. D.C Power supply unit used for providing alternative D.C supply

Figure 4.12: D.C Power supply unit
Image Source: www.alibaba.com

13. Electronic Board Cleaning Agents are used for cleaning the P.C.B after a liquid damage or during mobile phone servicing. Many technicians use Methylated spirits. This is not a good standard board cleaning agent because it contains toxic oils. Search for and obtain from any chemical vendor, Isopropyl Alcohol (IPA) which is a better non-oil cleaning agent for mobile phones. Thinner also serves as a good cleaning agent for PCBs. However peripheral component units must first be removed from the main board before it is applied.

14. Jumper Wires are also important for electrical connections between termination points. It is advisable to purchase the commercially available coated ones as seen in the picture below although one might pick some strands off from flexible electrical wire bundles.

Figure 4.13: Roll of Jumper wires

15. LCD/Touchscreen Machine Separator is a device used for separating damaged touchscreen digitizers from the LCD with ease.

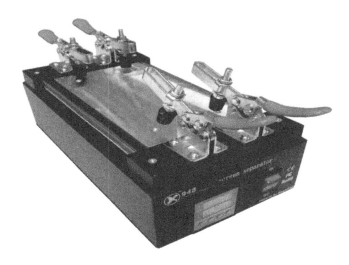

Figure 4.14: LCD/Touchscreen Separator machine

16. Screen Sucker: Used for lifting screens off the frame of a smartphone or tablet during screen removal process.

Figure 4.15: Touchscreen Suckers

17. Easy Draw Smartphone Schematic Diagrams Tool: This is a software tool that helps technicians access the component layout diagrams of smartphone electronic boards. With Easy Draw tool, you can simultaneously check out bitmap and schematic diagrams for different models like iPhones, iPad, Samsung, Xiaomi, Huawei, Gionee, Lenovo and so on.

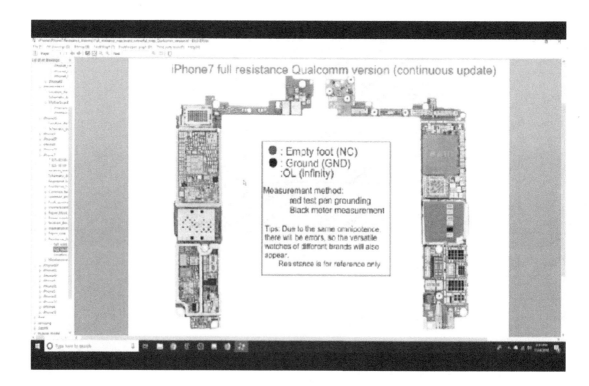

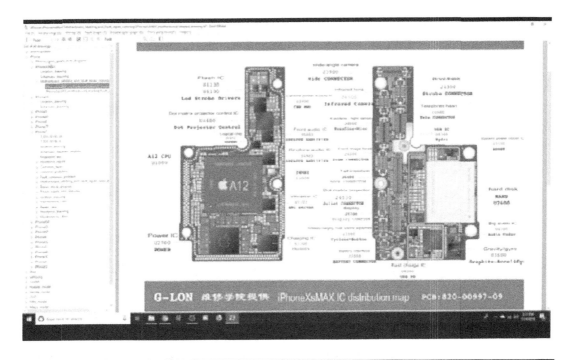

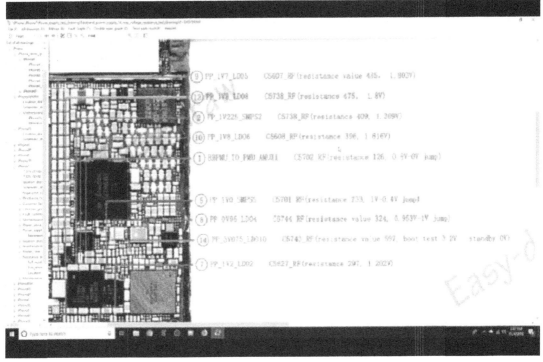

With this tool, the position of components, voltage and current values, resistance values, and even fault diagrams for common faults are laid out for easy fault diagnosis and correction. The interconnections between all the components are laid bare for one to see. See a few screenshots below;

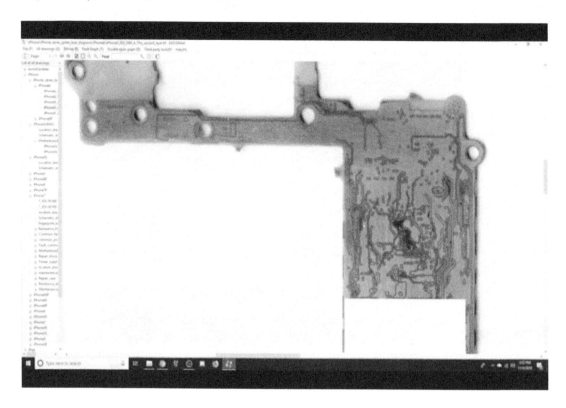

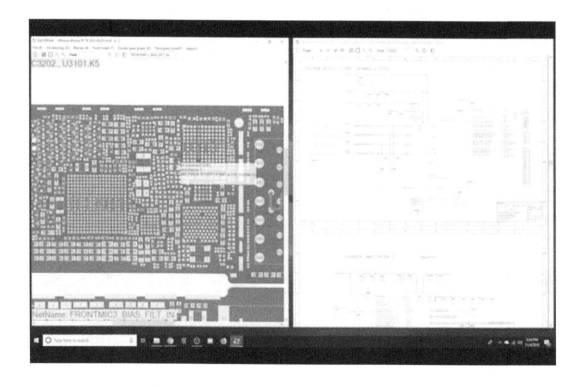

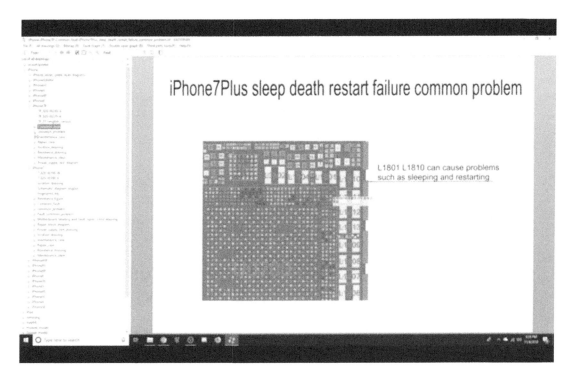

These are just a few snapshots to give insight into the features and types of drawings or schematics Easy Draw provides.

Finally, I will like to encourage a starter not to feel discouraged with the assumption that one must buy every tool or equipment before starting the business of repairs. The most basic requirement is having the technical knowledge and skills.

Tip

The tools required for 'Hardware Repairs' just like PC repairs are pretty simple and inexpensive. You can carry most of these tools in a small tool handbag or briefcase sized container with the exception of an SMD rework station and a computer (Desktop or Laptop for software repairs). The total cost of these smaller toolkits ranges between 3000-5000 Naira ($20-30) which is very affordable. The best way to maximize use of this book to learn is to purchase these tools and try out what you learn as you go through this book.

Chapter 5

Screen Replacement Procedures

Today's smartphones and tablets have more computing power than earlier computers that were bigger in size. As technology continues to advance, these handheld mobile device's components keep becoming smaller and smaller.

Prior to carrying out repairs, it is important to first identify the mobile device's manufacturer and model number. This is very important. Determining the authentic version of a device and its manufacturer is a key factor necessary for a successful replacement with the right parts. Information about a device was usually written at the back label underneath the battery in earlier models but with the recent sealed design for most smartphones and tablets today, only the brand logo is emblazoned at the back of the device while other technical information about the device can be found in the device's settings.

Disassembling and Reassembling a Device

With advancements in screen technology and having become a major feature as well as the most expensive invaluable part of any smartphone or tablet out there, honing the skill for efficient, neat and safe removal and replacement of screens is a major skill.

Apart from replacing damaged screens, removal and replacement of the sprawling frontal screen overlay of today's smartphones and tablets is a must before any other kind of repairs is to be carried out on the electronic motherboard.

It is mainly because of this skill-area that it became necessary to write an updated version of the first book, "*Mobile Phones and Tablets Repairs: A Complete Guide for Beginners and Professionals*". Therefore, this chapter would be exploring all avenues to teach, coach, guide and help the learner navigate through this herculean task which would be a daily routine determining either success or failure in the field. Before going further, keep in mind that everything learnt from this book is applicable to both smartphones and tablets

Figure 5.1: Sample Device Tear-down

As shown in the sample image above, until you are able to dismantle the entire coupling of a smartphone, separating every component attached to the motherboard and reattach everything back into a fully coupled and working device with no errors, damage or deformity, you are fifty percent not ready. **Required Tools**: A precision screwdriver set, casing openers, hot air soldering station or blow dryer, a sharp knife or razor blade.

Figure 5.2: Precision Screwdriver Sets

Rework Station (Any model)   Hair Dryer

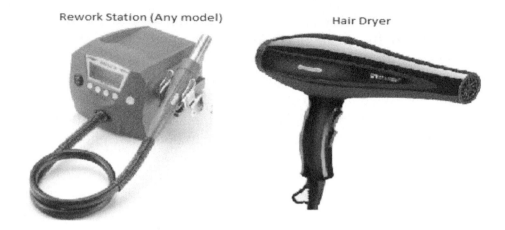

Dismantling Procedures

Each smartphone or tablet is unique in the way it is coupled together and the software it runs. The following is a general guideline for dismantling legacy either mobile phones, smartphones or tablets.

1. Turn the mobile device off as a first step.
2. Remove the back cover (for basic or feature mobile phones) of the phone you want to disassemble.
3. Remove the battery, SIM card, and if there is present a memory card. Be careful especially for models that have sliding side memory card slots. Smartphones and tablets have sliding side SIM card slots. Remove it as well.
4. Now, take a few moments to study the device's design. Observe the rear side of the device carefully for screws, screw-holes (usually stuffed neatly with cylindrical rubber paddings). If it is a smartphone or tablet, there is a ninety nine percent chance that the front screen needs to be removed to dismantle the device. In that case heat is required.
5. Next is to observe the demarcating slit that firmly couple the front and back casing of the device together. This is a definite feature on every mobile phone but smartphones and tablets have their entire screen (no upper casing) glued on the back casing or frame, forming a modular, sealed design.
6. Using the screw driver (for mobile phones), observe the type of Phillips screw head used. It could be a 3-point, 4-point or 5-point star

or pentalobe. Choose the screw bit that fits and remove the nuts one after the other while placing them carefully in a holder on your work table. Be careful not to misplace these nuts. Most screwdrivers usually have intrinsic electromagnetic properties which magnetize the nuts unto its body until removed for safe keeping.

7. If the device for which a screen is being replaced has cracked screen, it is best to prevent further cracks or even personal harm by taping over the glass with overlapping strips of tape.

8. When using the screen sucker to lift the screen up, don't go all the way. Create an opening where the plastic opener can slide in. Use the opener gradually to slide round the edges of the device while lifting the screen gradually.

Caution

If you are dealing with an iPhone product, carefully mark the screws and their locations as soon as you remove them. If you replace a nut into a location different from where it was removed, the screen may become damaged resulting into a blue screen condition.

Figure 5.3a: Back cover screw holes

Observe that when holding the device, your hand should grip the sides of the phone while the other holds the screw driver. Avoid bare palm touches on the board as static electric discharge from your palms can damage the motherboard. Standard practice is to buy and use anti-static wrist straps.

The four screw slots can be seen above the battery and two beside it left and right, making a total of six. In some cases there might be four screws at the four edges of the square section above the battery area covered with a clip-secured back cover which must first be removed before finding the screws, with another four screws downwards. The point is, your task is to locate the discreetly hidden screws securing the phone's casing together.

If you are working on legacy mobile phones, always keep in mind that these screws exist, tucked away in such a manner as to avoid being conspicuous to the untrained eye while ensuring a sleek, aesthetic less mechanical design. In cases where one fails to find any screws at the rear especially for the square or rectangular section above the battery compartment, know for sure that the screws are likely hidden within the front chassis cover right behind the screen or front cover casing of the device. For such designs the front cover casing has to be removed by sliding off (using the plastic casing opener) the clips holding it to the chassis and the back casing.

But for the more recent designs of smartphones and tablets, removing the front screen poses a challenge. iPhones are secured with side clips and two P2 pentalobe bottom screws near the charging port. With a good suction tool, you can lift off the screens out of the back frame after applying soft heat to soften the adhesive glue underneath the screen. However, Samsung and most smartphones use glue. We will get to that shortly.

Also, kindly note that removal of iPhone screens do compromise the waterproof seals. Therefore, ensure you have replacement seal before starting the removal and replacement process.

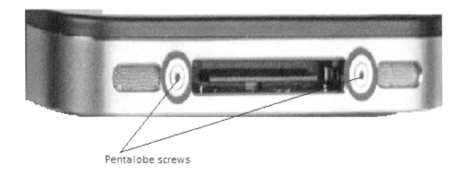

Pentalobe screws

Take a look below at a sample front casing with clips to understand what they are like.

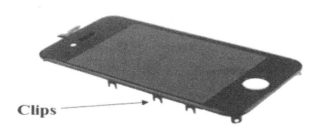

Figure 5.4: Sample casing side fixture clips

Figure 5.5 shows some common specimens of screw heads;

Figure 5.5: Screw heads

9. After dissecting the upper or lower casing from the chassis or the screen, cautiously watch out for flexible ribbon cable connectors that may be stuck to the casing body; may require immediate detachment; are probably attached to side keys(for screen, side volume control buttons, camera etc.). One needs to apply tact and keen observation when handling phones you have never disassembled before.

10. Carefully pick up any part (plastic or whatever) that falls off to the table and make an observatory note of where that part came off from. Like the Phillips nuts, place each item carefully in a safe container.

11. Next is to take another long look at the chassis with on-board peripheral components such as speakers, microphone and so on. Are there other tightly fixed Phillips screws? Take them out sequentially, taking note of which part is being held in what position. It gets easier as you go step by step. **Do not force anything out** - you have to keenly observe and you'll figure out whatever (glue or nuts) it is that holds it in that position. If glued, apply light heat to free it.

12. Note that the flexible ribbon cable connectors that plug certain components to the smartphone or tablet's motherboard are of different types. A hands-on practice with dummy phones will help to hone the skills on some models while figuring it out personally.

The above-listed are a summary of the general steps to take in disassembling any mobile device with specific tips for smartphones and tablets. To reassemble the components, a reverse order of similar steps taken during the dismantling process is repeated.

How to Use the Manual LCD Screen Separator Machine

A simple to use machine, the vacuum LCD separator machine uniformly spreads controlled heat across the length and breadth of the smartphone or tablet, drying out the glue that holds the screen firmly to the frame.

To use it to separate the digitizer from the LCD, take the following simple steps;

1. Switch the machine ON

2. Using the temperature adjustment buttons (up and down), set the temperature to 110 degrees Celsius.

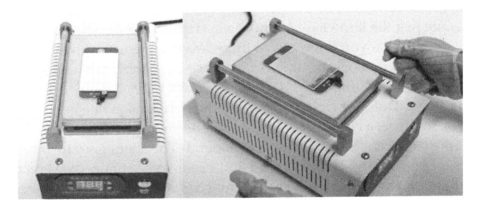

3. First align the perforated pad provided with the machine to the matrix of tiny holes on the flat surface. Then place the screen as seen in the image above. The pad prevents the screen from shifting or moving out of place.

4. When the heat has circulated enough, use a wire string (as seen in the image above (right) to slide between the demarcation of glass and LCD in a top to bottom fashion. Slide but do not lift upwards. Repeat the sliding motion again until the glass lifts up on its own.

Note that this same procedure is achieved by some using either hair dryer, rework station or any other source of heat.

Chapter 6

Board-Level Repairs and Micro-soldering

A good technician must become proficient in certain key skills before beginning to apply that knowledge on technical fault correction. The major difference between a mobile phone technician or most technicians and their clients is not just the knowledge of how a system works or what to do, but actually **doing** what you know. Most times, even some users already 'know' what could have gone wrong and in some cases, probably what needs to be done to correct the fault BUT THEY CANNOT **DO** IT.

Doing It and **Doing it right** therefore is the only reason one gets paid by a client. For instance, a client brings to his mobile smartphone and complains that people could not hear him at the other end. The client goes further to say his microphone or mouth-piece is bad and needs to be changed! (Maybe he picked that knowledge somewhere and maybe he is partially correct because changing it might not be the only solution). So you go thinking *'Hugh? Wait a minute why did you come to me with it then? You could as well have fixed it already!'*

The truth is, he/she cannot **Do (fix) It.** Your technical skill in the area of smartphone disassembling and reassembling will fetch you his or her money. You know what? It is an important and so delicate a skill that other electronic technicians (for bigger devices like TV, Radio etc.) still go after mobile phone technicians when their phones develop faults.

This brings us to the second skill - soldering. Most technicians who work on bigger motherboards like home electronics technicians do whack jobs when confronted with the tinier smartphone motherboards. Therefore, BGA and micro-electronic device soldering is a very important skill to be proficient in and constant practice with dummy boards is recommended.

The third skill a technician cannot do without is on the use of Multi-meters. Every electronic or electrical technical support personnel must be knowledgeable in this area to be distinctly more efficient. It is a skill that must be applied in their daily operations as technical solution providers especially if one understands electronic circuits and systems very well.

Understanding electronic circuits and the reading of circuit diagrams is another skill area technicians must pay strict attention to. Although what might pose a challenge to some persons interested in gaining in-depth appreciation of this skill area is either the lack of technical education, or a previous background in a study area that never included science. I encourage the reader not to lose heart about this. It is not mandatory but essential for a higher level of professionalism.

How to Use Multi-meter for Troubleshooting

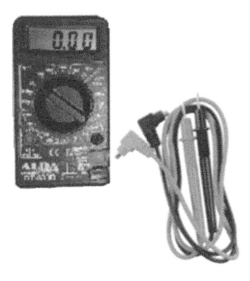

Figure 6.1: Digital Multi-meter

What is a Multi-meter?

A multi-meter is a device used commonly for diagnostic tracing in electrical or electronic circuits to confirm that expected voltages and currents are present at the right points in the circuit as well as resistance across component terminals. It is therefore used for measurement of voltage, resistance and current in electronics or electrical equipment as well as to test continuity between two points to verify if there are any breaks in the circuit or line.

There are two types of multi-meter;

+ Analog Multi-meter which has a needle style gauge.

+ Digital Multi-meter which has an LCD display with digital readout.

We shall rather focus on Digital multi-meters especially using the specimen type in the images shown below. There are other types in the market.

Meter Probes or Leads

- Probes are the handles used for holding the tip on any chosen testing point. The tapered end of the probe is called the tip and provides a connection to the test point.
- The meter's Red lead is connected to Voltage, Resistance or Amperage port and is considered the positive connection probe. There are usually two ports, one for lower currents and the other for high current measurements from 10 Amps and above.
- The meter's Black lead is always connected to the common port and is considered the negative connection probe.

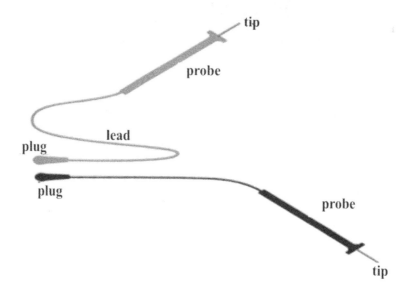

Figure 6.2: Digital Multi-meter probes

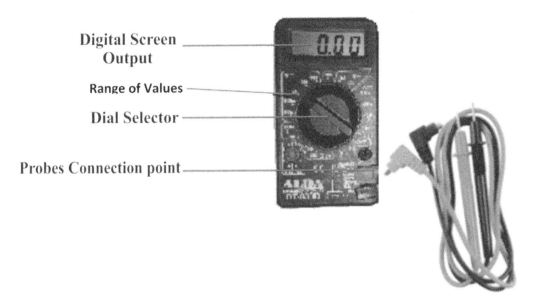

Figure 6.3: Digital Multi-meter

Understanding the Meter Calibration Parameters

Before we learn how to measure the various electrical quantities, it is important for the trainee to know the meaning of the numbers selected by the dial selector switch for any quantity being measured. Below is a magnified image of the calibrated surface of the meter;

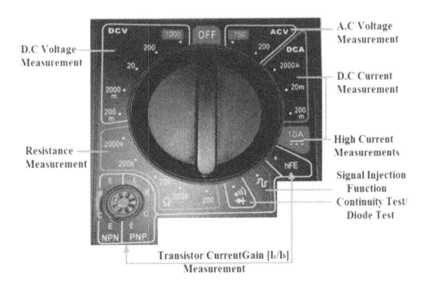

Each of the sections has a range of values similar to the prefixes used in the metric system such as **milli**-meter, **kilo**-meter etc. These prefixes are used just the same way for volts, ohms and amps – the units of measurement of electricity. Looking at the image above, you will notice the following;

m = milli

k = kilo

μ = micro

Symbols	Prefix Name	Numerical Equivalent	Mathematical Expression
m	milli	0.001	10^{-3}
μ	micro	0.000001	10^{-6}
k	kilo	1, 000	10^{3}
M	Mega	1, 000, 000	10^{6}
G	Giga	1, 000, 000, 000	10^{9}

Table 6.1: Metric system and units

There are others but let me stick to the multi-meter before us. Some multi-meters have an "auto" range feature that selects the range automatically thereby removing the mental hassle of manually determining the dial selector point. Let me explain each calibration range below, specifically for the small digital meter in the image here. Other multi-meters might have other range of values within its tolerance threshold.

D.C Voltage Measurement Block: The range of values here are from 200 millivolts to 1000 volts D.C, comparable to a linear scale from (-x) to (0) to (+x) axis on a Cartesian co-ordinate. When measuring battery voltages, the dial selector switch should point to this block. For accurate resolution of values, point to the value range closest to the expected value being measured. For instance, a smartphone battery ranges between 3.6V to 4.2V maximum. The closest to this value is "20" (20v d.c) on the multi-meter DCV block. Point the dial selector to '20' in order to measure the battery's voltage. Most Digital Multi-meters are auto-polarity sensing devices. This means that for such types you do not have to worry about having the Red lead on the positive and the Black Lead on the Neutral or negative of the battery or other terminals. It just gives you the accurate reading.

A.C Voltage Measurement Block: The range of values here is between 0V to 750V AC (with subdivision into 0-200 and 201-750). For any value between 0 – 200, there will be an output or the display will be "1" or out-of-range signified by "OL" (overload) in others. When this happens, move the dial upwards in the range (in this case to 750) and test. To measure AC voltage, we place the Red lead into the "VΩmA" port and black lead into the "COM" port. Turn the dial selector switch to ACV or V~ in some models. If it is a manual ranging meter, set it for the proper range. For example, the meter would be set to the 200V range if 110V is to be measured but set to the 750V range to measure a 220V AC outlet. If you have an auto-ranging meter you only need to set the function to ACV. It is always good practice to connect the black probe first, followed by the red probe.

D.C Current Measurement Block: This function also measures DC current and therefore is selected to measure current values. There are two ranges of values for measuring up to a maximum 200milliamps and for values up to maximum 10A. When measuring higher current values, the red probe has to be moved to port 1. See the image in fig. 4.8 below;

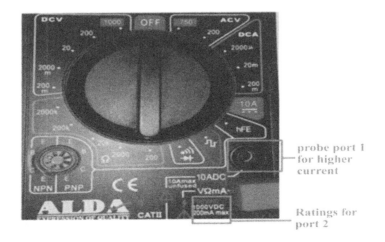

Figure 6.4: Digital Multi-meter probe connection

Resistance Measurement Block: The resistance calibration follows a range of values from 0-200 ohms up to maximum 2,000k (2, 000, 000 ohms) or 2MΩ. K is kilo which is thousand. 2000k is equivalent to 2000 x k (1000) which is 2, 000,000. During measurement, it is advisable to begin from the lowest range and move up if the output is "1" or "OL" indicating out-of-range.

Continuity Test/Diode Test: This selection point is for continuity testing with audible alarm to aid in troubleshooting without taking your eyes off the PCB. It also doubles for testing Diodes' forward resistance.

Transistor Current Gain Testing: This function block is used to measure the current gain of a transistor which is the ratio of its output collector current I_c to the input base current I_b. On the left side are slots for inserting the three pins of a transistor, either an NPN or PNP, marked EBC (top-to-down); ECB (bottom-up) for any type of transistor test. It may therefore serve also to detect the right pin combinations or type of transistor since a gain output can only appear on the display when properly situated.

Signal Injection Function: This function when selected is used for injecting a square wave of about 2V peak at a frequency of between 30 and 40 HZ into an audio device. Mostly used for testing whether an amplifier is functioning or not. To use this function;
- Turn the dial selector to the Signal Injection Function
- Using the negative black meter probe, touch the ground of the circuit being measured.
- At the point in the circuit where the test signal is to be injected, touch the red probe tip.

Taking Actual Readings and Measurements

Measurement of Voltage

Voltage (V) is the unit of electrical pressure force. One volt is defined as the potential difference needed to cause one amp of current to pass through one ohm of resistance. Voltage is broken up into 2 classes - AC and DC. Alternating Current (AC) is the Utility supply voltage (220-240Va/c) in Nigeria while Direct Current (DC) is battery voltage.

To carry out measurement;

- First, be careful not to touch any other electronic component within the equipment and do not short (bridge) the tips together while connected to anything else.
- To measure voltage, connect the probes in parallel between the two points where the measurement is to be made. The multi-meter provides a parallel pathway so it needs to be of a high resistance to allow as little current to flow through it as possible.

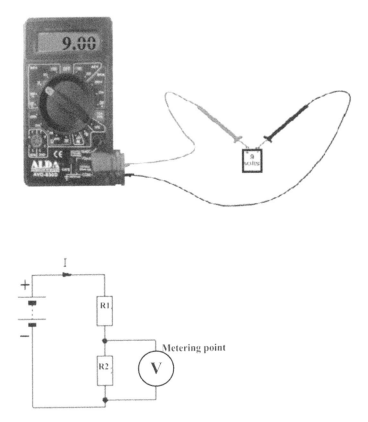

Figure 6.5: Voltage Measurement

Measurement of Resistance and Continuity

Resistance is the opposition to current flow and is measured in ohms. To carry out a resistance measurement;

- Disconnect the power source before testing.
- Remove the component or part from the system (circuit board) before testing.

- Measure using the lowest calibration point,; if 0Ω, move to the next.
- Testing for continuity is used to verify if a circuit, wire or fuse is "closed" or "open" circuited (a break).
- Audible sound is heard if the circuit, wire, or fuse is complete (continuous end-to-end) but silent if there is a break in the circuit, wire or fuse. In analog multi-meters the range is between 0 to ∞ (infinity is high resistance). "Closed" i.e. 0Ω while "open" is ∞.

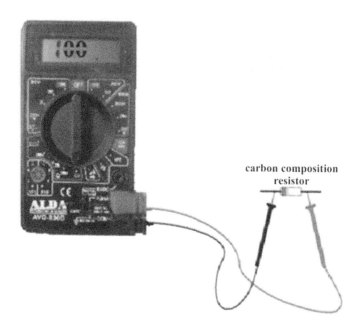

Figure 6.6: Resistance Measurement

Measurement of Current

Current is the flow of charge through a component or conductor and the unit of measurement is the Ampere (Amps), A. To measure current;
- First, disconnect the power source before measurement.
- Disconnect the completed circuit system at one of its ends.
- Place the multi-meter in series with the circuit (see image below).
- Reconnect the power source and turn it ON.
- Select the highest current calibration setting and work your way down.

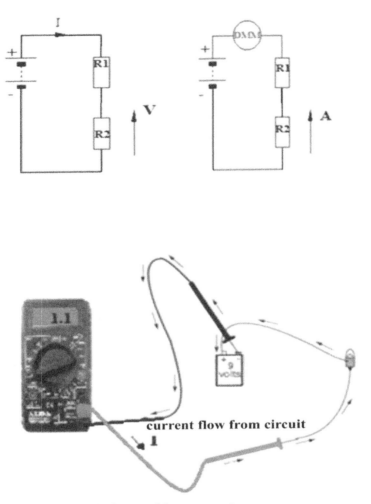

Figure 6.7: Current Measurement

Review

❖ A meter capable of testing or measuring voltage, current, and resistance is called a *multi-meter*.

❖ When measuring Voltage, the multi-meter must be connected to two reference points in a circuit in order to obtain a good reading. Be careful not to bridge the probe's tips while measuring voltage, as this will create short-circuits!

❖ Never carry out resistance measurement or test for continuity with a multi-meter on a circuit that is energized.

❖ When measuring Current, the multi-meter must be connected in a circuit in such a way that the electrons have to flow *through* the meter.

❖ Multi-meters have practically no resistance between their leads. This is intended to allow electrons to flow through the meter with the least possible difficulty. If this were not the case, the meter would add extra resistance in the circuit, thereby affecting the current or values.

Symbols	Terms	Symbols	Terms
~	AC Voltage	+	Positice
▦	DC Voltage	–	Negative
Hz	Hertz	μF	MicroFarad
⏚	Ground	μ	Micro
⊣⊢	Capacitor	m	Milli
Ω	Ohms	K	Kilo
▶⊢	Diode	M	Mega
•)))	Audible Continuity	OL or "1"	Overload/Infinity

Table 6.2: Symbols and their meanings

Standard Values for Some Peripheral Components

The following peripheral components attached to the motherboard of smartphones and tablets have been proven to have a range of resistance values during their optimum performance lifecycle.

1. Microphone (Mouth Piece) - $700 – 1700\ \Omega \pm 100$
2. Speakers (Earpiece)   - $30 – 33\ \Omega \pm 3$
3. Ringers   - $8 – 10\ \Omega \pm 1$
4. Vibrators   - $8\text{-}16\ \Omega \pm 1$

These are optimum performance values. Any value below the minimum or above the maximum would mean that the component has either failed or is depreciating to a non-functional or non-optimal state even if it is still in use and working.

How to Test Various Components

There are analyzers for carrying out the task of testing various electronic components but the expense can be difficult to justify for the average technician especially a start-up. If you take a survey worldwide, of field or bench technicians, you will discover that their most-used piece of test equipment is a Digital Multi-meter (Analog multi-meter for some). These versatile devices can be used to test and diagnose a wide range of circuits and components. Since this book promotes technical entrepreneurship, we shall discuss how to use a Digital Multi-meter in details.

Switches

To test switches:

i.   Determine the type of switch you are faced with.

ii.   Put the multi-meter in continuity test ("diode symbol") mode with buzzer (beep) alert.

iii.   Identify the switch's PCB (Printed Circuit Board, also called the motherboard) terminals.

iv.   For a two-terminal switch in normal (OFF) state, test for continuity between both terminals. If a beep confirms continuity, replace the switch.

v.   If there is no continuity in the OFF state, place both probes each on either terminals and push or operate the switch.

vi.   If there is a beep (continuity indicator) when the switch is operated, the switch is ok. If there is no beep (no continuity), the switch is damaged. Change the switch.

vii.   For a four-terminal switch, note that only two polarities exist from the electrical supply. Therefore, there is only 2 test points. The extra two terminals are usually either for balance or due to other switch design considerations. Identify the test point terminals (a pair is continuous with each other but separate from the other pair) and repeat procedure (iv) to (vi) above.

Microphones

To test Microphones:

i.   Put the multi-meter in continuity test ("diode symbol") mode with buzzer (beep) alert.

ii.   Microphones are two-terminal components. Place the positive (+) probe to the terminal connected to the PCB's positive (+) pad. It is usually marked on the PCB. Place the negative (-) probe on its negative (-) terminal too.

iii. The value displayed should range between 700~1700Ω ± 100

iv. For any value below 600Ω or above 1800Ω replace.

Speakers

To test Speakers:

i. Put the multi-meter in continuity test ("diode symbol") mode with buzzer (beep) alert.

ii. Speakers are 2-terminal components. Place the positive (+) probe on the terminal connected to the PCB's positive (+) pad. It is usually marked on the PCB. In some cases the terminals are PVC coated red (+) and black (-) wires. Place the negative (-) probe on the speakers' negative (-) terminal too.

iii. The value displayed should range between 30~33Ω ± 3

iv. For any value below 27Ω or above 36Ω replace.

Ringers

To test Ringers:

i. Place the multi-meter in continuity test ("diode testing") mode with buzzer (beep) alert.

ii. Ringers are two-terminal components. Place the positive (+) probe on the terminal connected to the PCB's positive (+) pad. It is usually marked on the PCB. In some cases the terminals are PVC coated red (+) and black (-) wires. Place the negative (-) probe on its negative (-) terminal too.

iii. The value displayed on the meter should range between 9~10Ω ± 1

iv. For any value below 8Ω or above 11Ω replace.

Vibrators

To test Vibrators:

i.   Place the multi-meter in continuity ("diode symbol") test mode with buzzer (beep) alert.

ii. Vibrators are 2-terminal components. Place the positive (+) probe to the terminal connected to PCB's positive (+) pad. It is usually marked on the PCB. In some cases the terminals are PVC coated red (+) and black (-) wires. Place the negative (-) probe to its negative (-) terminal too.

iii. The value displayed on the meter should range between 9~15Ω ± 1

iv. For any value below 8Ω or above 16Ω replace.

Resistors

Resistors are passive two-terminal electrical components that provide electrical resistance as a circuit element. In an earlier section, we examined how to measure resistances.

To test Resistors:

i.   Put the multi-meter in Resistance test mode.

ii. Resistor terminals do not have polarity. The probes can be placed either way on each of the terminals. The PCB must be disconnected from the power supply mains.

iii. Place the positive (+) probe on one of its terminals connected to the PCB. Place the negative (-) probe on its other terminal and take readings.

iv. The dial selector switch should be turned to the lowest scale on the resistance calibrator before starting the measurement.

v.   Before testing a resistor, it is better to establish what the accurate value for a specific resistor should be either from a schematic diagram or as written on the board.

vi. Continue to scale up until a unit value is obtained.

vii. Test results must not be too low such that the value approximates to zero ohms. That will indicate a value equivalent to a short circuit (like a jumper). Exception is for resistors used as fuses. Also if the results are too high, this may be indicative of an open circuit resistor (broken) or a resistor that has acquired a higher value. This is a possible sign of a fault.

Diodes

Diodes are two-terminal electronic devices that allows current through them ONLY in one direction (anode to cathode) but blocks the flow of current through them from the other direction (cathode to anode). This simply means that it has low resistance to the flow of current in one direction and high (or infinite) resistance in the other direction.

Semi-conductor signal diodes are the most common occurring types in smartphone circuit-boards. Also pertinent to note is the difference between convention current flow and electron flow. It is explained later in Chapter 6 "Electronic fundamentals"

Convention current is the flow of current from the positive (+) terminal to the negative (-) terminal while electrons flow from the negative (-) cathode to the positive (+) anode in a diode.

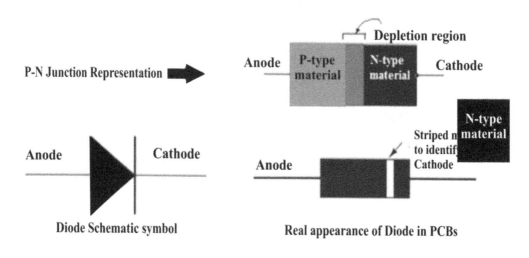

Figure 6.8: Diode Symbols

To test diodes for defect:

i.   Put the multi-meter in continuity test ("diode symbol") mode with buzzer (beep) alert.

ii. Place the positive (+) probe to the Anode terminal connected to the PCB pad and place the negative (-) probe to the Cathode (-) terminal marked with a stripe.

iii. **Note:** The output read on the meter display should differ for various diodes according to the diode's rated forward resistance. This test is not meant for taking value readings. It is simply a PASS or FAIL test.

iv.   If there is an output value in this direction, switch the probes to the opposite terminals and there should be no reading (infinite resistance) in this state for a good diode.

v.   If there are output values in both cases, the diode is shorted.

vi.   If there was no reading (infinite resistance) in both cases, the diode is open circuited (therefore bad).

vii.   A good diode should ONLY read forward resistance when the positive probe (+) is on the ANODE and the negative (-) probe is on the Cathode and no reading when the probes are reversed.

Transistors

Transistors are composed of semiconductor materials with at least three terminals for connection to an external circuit. Depending on the internal doping substance, a transistor could be a Bipolar Junction Transistor (BJT) or a Metal Oxide Silicon Field Effect Transistor (MOSFET)

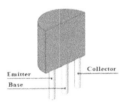

Figure 6.9: Transistor

There are two BJT types of transistors;

- NPN Transistors
- PNP Transistors

To test a BJT transistor, we have to view the component as two back-to-back diodes connected together in either of these ways;

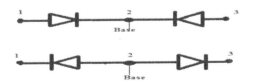

Figure 6.10: Transistor equivalent using 2 back-to-back diodes

Either of the sides (left and right) could be determined to be the Collector or Emitter respectively.

Method 1

Using the digital multi-meter, identify the three pins in the transistor image above with numbers one, two, and three. This test is for Bipolar Junction transistors (BJT);

i. Select continuity ("diode testing") test point on the meter with buzzer alert.

ii. **Note:** The Readout on the meter's display would differ for various diodes according to the diode's rated forward resistance. This test is not meant for taking readings of the diode's resistance value. It is simply a PASS or FAIL test.

iii. Place the positive probe (+) at pin 2 of the transistor. Do not assume that the middle pin (2) is the "Base" by default.

iv. Place the negative (-) probe alternately on the two side pins - 1 and 3. Check if there is a value displayed on the meter. If the probe's polarity combination [pins 2(+)/1(-)] reads out a value and [pins 2(+)/3(-)] reads out a value too, then both junctions have forward resistances for the two back-to-back diode's left and right arms.

v. Alternate by replacing the positive probe on pin 2 with the negative probe. Did pin 2(-)/1(+) and 2(-)/3(+) give any reading or infinite resistance? If both arms (left and right) gave no reading, the transistor is in good condition. Next is to determine what type of transistor is being tested (NPN or PNP). If a value was displayed (forward resistance) only when the **P**ositive probe was at a particular pin (common point, "Base"), while the **N**egative probe was alternated between the other two pins then it is NPN. When reversed and a forward resistance is displayed only when the **N**egative probe is place at a common (Base) pin, and the **P**ositive probe is alternated between the other two pins, then it is PNP.

vi. After checking with the positive probe at pin 2, always reverse-check with the negative probe on the same pin 2. Pin 2 will not always be the Base (common). The "Base" could be any of the pins and is the pin which when used as the starting test point (+ or – probe) will give a forward resistance reading when the other polarity (+ or -) probe is placed alternately on the other two pins.

vii. Repeat the same procedure with each of the three pins in focus (reference + or -), to determine which pin provides a common point from which the other pins records a forward resistance with the other polarity.

Method 2

Another method for testing a transistor is by reading the output voltage. Any contrary readout from the following values listed below would mean that the transistor being tested is bad. Follow the procedure below.

i. Remove the transistor from the circuit board for accurate test results.

ii. The Emitter-Base junction typically has a slightly higher voltage drop than the Collector-Base junction. This is a way to distinguish one from the other.

iii. Start with testing the Base-to-Emitter junction. Place the positive probe of the multi-meter on the BASE (B) of the transistor. Place the negative probe on the EMITTER (E) of the transistor. For a good NPN transistor, the meter should display a voltage drop between 0.45V and 0.9V. If you are testing a PNP transistor, you should see "1" (Infinite Resistance).

iv. Test the Base-to-Collector junction. Place the positive probe on the BASE (B) and place the negative probe on the COLLECTOR (C). For a good NPN transistor, the meter should display a voltage drop between 0.45V and 0.9V. If you are testing a PNP transistor, you should see "1" (Infinite Resistance).

v. Test the Emitter-Base junction. Place the positive probe on the EMITTER (E) and the negative probe on the BASE (B) of the transistor. For a good NPN transistor, you should see infinite resistance. If you are testing PNP transistor, the meter should display a voltage drop between 0.45V and 0.9V.

vi. Next test the Collector-Base junction. Place the positive probe on the COLLECTOR (C) of the transistor and the negative probe on the BASE (B) of the transistor. For a good NPN transistor, you should see "1" (Infinite Resistance).If you are testing a PNP transistor, the meter should display a voltage drop between 0.45V and 0.9V.

vii.   Next, test the Collector- Emitter junction. Place the positive probe on the COLLECTOR (C) and the negative probe on the EMITTER (E). A good NPN or PNP transistor will display "1" (Infinite Resistance). Reverse the polarity (Positive to Emitter terminal and Negative to Collector terminal). A good NPN or PNP transistor should read "1" or Infinite Resistance.

Capacitors

To carry out tests on capacitors in smartphone PCBs, we have to first consider its property. Capacitors store energy as an electrostatic field. They are found in mobile devices, of various colors, forms and types. They include;

- Non-Electrolytic Capacitors – are light black (dark grey), yellow or brown in color. They are non-polarized (no positive (+) or Negative (-) terminal marking).
- Electrolytic Capacitors – are usually either orange in color with brown strip at one end or black in color with a white strip on one end in smartphones. The side with the strip is Positive (+) while the other side is Negative (-).

The reason for the description above is this; testing for capacitor failure in smartphones or tablets includes observing the coloration that occurs when they burn out. Capacitors become defective in two ways;

- Short circuit
- Open circuit

To carry out testing for short circuit defect;

i.   Set the multi-meter to its minimum resistance scale.
ii.   For **electrolytic capacitors,** connect the negative (-) probe to the capacitor's positive (+) terminal and the positive (+) probe to the negative (-) terminal.
iii. If the meter reads zero ohms initially and goes to infinity ('1' in some digital multi-meters) then it is not short-circuited (shorted).
iv.   For **non-electrolytic capacitors** like ceramic and other capacitor types with a capacitance less than 1.0 μF, the meter reading will remain motionless i.e. infinite resistance.

v.   If it is shorted, the meter reading will tend to zero ohms.

vi.   For bigger capacitors, the standard thing to do is to remove one lead of its terminals from the PCB circuit. But for mobile devices, do not do that. The idea is to test the ability of the capacitor being tested; for it to behave in accordance with its charge storing capability. When a D.C supply is applied to its terminals, the voltmeter output will simply reflect the supply voltage output after a while. But if the capacitor is leaking or if the capacitor has shorted, the voltmeter reading will jump high and then drop low again although not to zero. However, if the meter registers no increase in value or jump at all, then the capacitor is either open or the capacitance is too low to register a result.

vii. For smartphone or tablet's capacitors, clean the PCB to ground the capacitors and neutralize all residual charge. If the target for testing has any charge, bridge the terminals to discharge it. Then, apply voltage from the power supply for 20 seconds to the PCB. Test again to confirm if it acquires charge from the supply as in (vi) above.

Inductors

Inductors are simply made up of a coil of wire wound on an armature or soft iron core. The best test to check whether an inductor is good or not is by testing the inductor's resistance with your multi-meter;

i.   Set the multi-meter's dial selector switch to ohmmeter (resistance) setting.

ii.   There are no polarity considerations with respect to resistance measurement. Place the (+) and (-) probes each on one terminal of the inductor.

iii. The inductor should read a very low resistance across its terminals, only a few ohms. If an inductor reads a high resistance, it is defective and should be replaced in the circuit.

iv.   If an inductor is reading very, very small resistance value, less than an ohm (very close to 0Ω), this may be a sign that it is shorted. Functional inductors normally read a few ohms, greater than 1Ω and usually less than 10Ω. This is a healthy range for an inductance value. Any value outside this range is normally a sign that the inductor is bad.

Testing Integrated Circuits (ICs) On Mobile Phone PCBs

The Power IC and CPU

To test these powerful chips, we use the following measurements deduced from normal values in functional mobile devices. *Note that these are deduced from years of field service experience. These are not to be construed as scientifically proven values.* Using a D.C power supply unit;

i. Adjust the voltage setting of the DC Power Supply to 4.2V D.C.
ii. Place the positive probe of the D.C Power Supply unit on the positive (+) terminal of the Battery Connector of the mobile phone and the negative Probe to the battery connector's negative (-) terminal.
iii. Check the D.C Ampere reading. If the DC Ampere is over 6A, then either the Power IC or CPU is damaged.
iv. First replace the Power IC.
v. If the problem is not solved, replace the CPU.
vi. If there is 0A reading on the display, then there could be a problem with any of the following;
   - Battery Connector
   - Power Switch current supply track or
   - RF Crystal oscillator
vii. If the current on the Ammeter reading is below 2A, there may be a software problem or a dead RTC (Real Time Clock) battery.
viii. If there is a beep sound from the D.C Power Supply machine, then there exists a short-circuit problem with the mobile device.

Advanced BGA Soldering Techniques

Soldering skills is one skill you cannot do without if you want to function as a good technical support provider. One action you must take is to practice.

Practice! Practice!! Practice!!! You have to practice until you perfect the skills.

What is Soldering?

Soldering is the process of jointing two terminals together using molten solder. Solder is a metal alloy of lead and Tin. The necessary tools required are;

1. The soldering iron or rework station - Use a 25W iron for small jobs and 100W for larger jobs. The soldering station has a variable temperature iron which is safer for boards as the tip temperature is adjusted to suit the job size.
2. Soldering wire – made of Lead and Tin alloy
3. Soldering paste/flux – is an additive that facilitates the soldering process by removing and preventing oxidation thereby improving the wetting or melting characteristics of the liquid solder.
4. Tweezers or clamp – Use tweezers or clamp to hold the components during the process as the components are very small.
5. Cutter/ Needle-nosed Plier.

Take a look at some needed tools images in fig. 6.11.

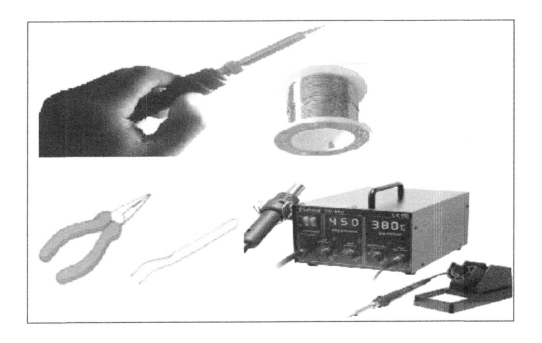

Figure 6.11: Soldering Tools

Soldering Procedure

Soldering, deals with the welding of both surface-mount and 'through-hole' components which are directly pressed into printed circuit boards (PCBs). These components have leads or wires that are either surface-mounted, passed through a hole in the board, or soldered to the copper-plated pad around the hole.

There are different techniques for soldering various components on the electronic board but the general principle governing the soldering process are as follows and will suffice;

- To solder a component into the PCB, use a tweezer or tong to place or hold the component in place, which in most cases are small miniature devices. Then, with one hand holding the soldering iron, place the iron's tip first on the pad (point of contact) while holding the solder wire on the other hand directed at the tip of the iron at the joint between the PCB and the component's terminal. This way, the hand holding the solder wire controls the amount of solder melted into the joint as it is withdrawn from the joint. See image below.
- A clamp can be used to hold the board in place (recommended) or it can just be placed on the work table while the component is soldered.

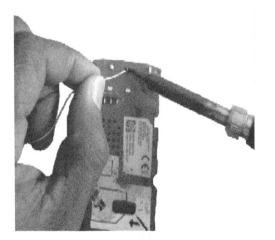 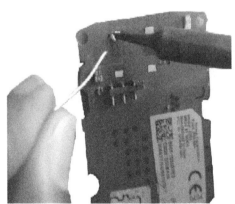

A. Feed the solder to the iron tip   B. Stop feed by withdrawing feed-hand

- Prepare the components to be soldered. For micro-sized smartphones or tablets, use the heat from the iron to moisten the terminals or contact points with small lead. Then, use cleaning agent to wipe the surfaces to achieve a neat soldering process. For bigger components, bend the component's leads correctly and carefully to avoid damage, and fit into the PCB board's contact point or pad.
- Next, "tin" the solder. This is done by melting a small blob of solder on the soldering iron's bit (tip). This process is called Tinning the bit" as it helps to improve heat flow from the iron to the lead and pad, safeguarding the board from excessive heat.

- Make solder balls with the iron and lead on the work table.
- Use the iron's tip to pick a lead ball. Place the soldering iron's tip with the tiny lead blob or ball on it, on the interface between the pad and lead, making sure it touches both the lead and pad.

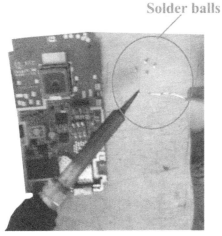

1. Create solder balls

2. Lifting a ball with iron tip

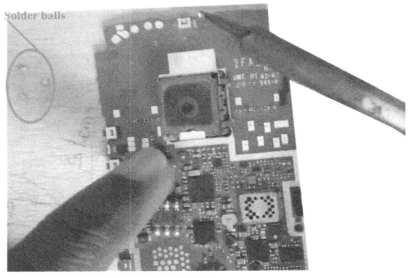

3. Placing the ball on a joint-in this case a switch terminal

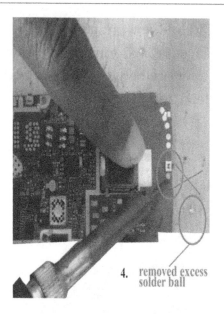

4. removed excess solder ball

5. perfect finish

Carefully apply solder on the appropriate location. Remember to prop the iron in a safe standing position when not in use to avoid burns or damage to useful surrounding components.

- Feed the right quantity of solder on the interface between the PCB pad and the component's contact pins and allow it to cool. Remove excess solder if there is any. This should not take more than a second as the molten solder easily solidifies once heat source is removed.
- If the solder does not melt easily on the jointing area, it is due to insufficient heat transfer to the jointing surface or due to a dirty surface.
- Remember to stop feeding the solder to the jointing terminal by removing the soldering lead wire. No more than a drop of lead is necessary for a good joint though it varies depending on the size and type of component. But the soldering-wire feed-hand controls what quantity is fed to a joint.
- Ensure that the iron is quickly moved out of the jointing surface as soon as possible because excessive heat on a joint can easily damage the pad(contact terminals) on which the component is to be jointed. Likewise, the component might get damaged due to excessive heating. Therefore, move quickly. The level of heat on the board can be gauged by using a finger to feel the board temperature.
- A good joint will normally appear shiny, smooth and cone shaped, otherwise it might result to a "cold" or dry joint with dull, gravel-like,

rough and frosty look. Visible indications tell if a joint is good. The solder should melt and merge with the components' contacts to form an alloy with the metal surface. The jointed solder should coat the component's surface in an even distribution. It should neither be too little nor too much.

- While carrying out the soldering process, clean off oxidation from the tip of the iron at regular intervals to aid heat transfer. After a good joint is made, make sure you allow the joint to cool before moving the components.

How to Use the Rework Station

A Rework station is a soldering machine used for carrying out high precision soldering jobs including removal and replacement of motherboard components. The name 'Rework' is derived from the fact that it is used to 'repeat work' (soldering) that has been done previously on-board, during the manufacturing of the PCB.

Rework stations have hot air guns or blowers which blow out hot air for use to either "heat" ICs (Chips) or to replace them. The heating process is meant to cause the solder holding the contact pins of the components fixed on the motherboard to soften and cool, to repair joints that have dried or broken. When ICs get disconnected from the circuit board, faults occur within the system.

Supposing for instance, the BGA (Ball Graphics Array) lead contacts of an IC (Integrated Circuit) which serves the purpose of distributing power (Power IC) throughout the motherboard, have become dry, rusted or broken, it would lead to the smartphone not powering ON. If the IC is related to charging, the battery will no longer be charged through the phone. SMD (Surface Mount Device) ICs also experience oxidation or rusting of their terminals but it is less prevalent and easily repaired with the soldering iron.

When using the rework station, there are two knobs of interest for optimum performance. Adjusting these knobs for the best heat transfer setting required is important. The variable temperature setting has a range of temperatures in degrees Celsius. The air pressure setting has its own calibration clockwise from low to high. There are also rework stations that have no digital display with just low to high calibrated knobs. Ensure that the blower does not function without adequate accompanying air. If you run the machine at increased temperature settings without commensurate air adjustment, the blower filament will get damaged.

IC BGA Soldering and Repair

Adjust temperatures relative to the operation being carried out;

Re-flow Soldering

BGA ICs usually malfunction due to wear and tear or corrosion of their mounting solder balls. Any crack in the solder that disconnects the PCB track from the IC will cause the chip to malfunction. Because of the tightly packed space underneath the ICs, it is easy for liquids to get trapped and cause corrosion. Sometimes, severe impact on the phone due to rough handling causes cracks in the solder ball point terminals of the ICS.

Therefore, to repair faults associated with the ICs, a hot air stream from the rework station is used to molten the solder balls and as they cool, they reconnect properly to both the PCB and the chip. To achieve this, controlled hot air is channeled to the IC. During this process, it is required to clean the underside of the IC by channeling cleaning fluid underneath and using air pressure from the blower to force out the fluid mixed with dirt. Repeat the process for as many times as possible until only clear fluid is expelled. Apply soldering paste and repeat the same process. During this time, the combined soldering paste and heat acts together to repair the solder balls. While channeling the heat, at intervals apply a light downward pressure on the chip with the thumb. This will help to bond the ball contacts and also aid to gauge the level of heating being applied. If it is excessive, it will burn the thumb. Use cleaning fluid to expel any residue of soldering paste when the process is concluded. Note that it is important to do this as soldering paste residue can cause overheating of the chip during normal operation of the phone due to heat energy dissipation.

This procedure above is to be applied after the normal dry heating process fails to correct an identified malfunctioning IC as well as before an outright removal, re-balling and replacement process is carried out.

How to Replace a BGA Chip(IC) On the PCB

After re-balling the ball contacts of the IC, position it on the PPCB using a tweezer and apply a hot air stream to the overall chip assembly. The solder balls underneath the chip will melt. The solder alloy's composition coupled with the controlled soldering temperature applied is such that the solder does not completely melt down and flow together, but stays semi-liquid, allowing each ball to distinctly stand away from its neighbors. Surface tension causes the molten solder to hold the IC package in the correct alignment with the circuit board, while the solder cools and solidifies

How to Swap a Faulty Component (ICs)

Applying very high temperatures with moderate air pressure to avoid blowing away relevant components around the operation area, is how a chip is removed from the PCB. The faulty component being removed can be destroyed in this case since it is of no use anymore. But when removing a good component for a swap, which needs to be re-balled and reused in another motherboard, adequate care and tact is to be applied.

When using such very high temperatures, ensure that you do not apply heat for long durations on the circuit-board as excessive heat spreading all over the motherboard may damage components with low withstand temperature. Be snappy about the process, using a tweezer to apply an upward pull to the component. The pull should not be such as to forcefully detach the component when the solder has not melted, else it will damage the ball point terminals on the motherboard.

Faulty Component (ICs) Removal, Re-Balling and Re-Use

The rework station comes with different sizes of nozzles. Choose the appropriate nozzle size depending on the location of the component within a particular surface area.

For any sparsely populated (surrounding electronic components like resistors, capacitors, diodes etc.) surface area and chip size, choose a bigger nozzle while the reverse is the case for a smaller nozzle.

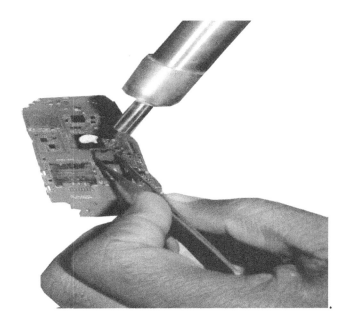

The faulty IC is removed using moderate temperatures, balancing the need to remove the chip without damaging it within the duration of heat transfer. Applying very high temperatures for a shorter duration than a moderately high temperature for a longer duration in the removal process takes a sound measure of good judgment. To aid the heat transfer process and protect the terminal pads connecting the component to the circuit-board from getting damaged as you apply the upward pull with the tweezer, apply soldering flux. The soldering flux should be applied at the edges of the IC before heating or removing it.

Bear in mind that the air pressure applied must be commensurate with increasing temperatures as a dry heat transfer will lead to charring or burning the component. Finally, take note of the markings on the top of the IC being removed. A dot mark usually serves as a guide for the IC's pin orientation when placing it in position. It is called a Nose Point.

 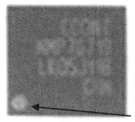 Nose Point (Dot mark)

Figure 6.12: IC

Upon successful de-soldering of the component, clean the underside with a brush and cleaning fluid, then apply flux or soldering paste. Using the soldering iron, create tiny blobs of soldering lead with which the ball joint matrix on the underside of the IC is re-balled.

Applying excessive quantity of lead will muddy up the multiple grid array. Flux also helps to disjoint any coagulation of solder across the terminals, causing a bridge or short. After re-balling all ball points on the underside of the IC and the equivalent ball points on the circuit-board, you can run hot stream of air over both surfaces and allow it to cool and set. Clean up the surface with brush and cleaning fluid, and inspect it be sure that all the tracks are separated from each other without any solder debris joining together any two terminals.

To re-solder the component back to the PCB, apply fresh soldering flux on both surfaces - the ball points on the underside of the IC and the motherboard surface. Use the tweezer to pick up the IC and place according to the original placement mark or Nose Point and apply hot air. This time, a downward pressure should be applied to stick the component in place.

CAUTION

When working on contact pads of motherboards (the shiny copper contact points or pad on which a component is soldered) do not apply excessive heat especially with fluxes. It usually flakes them out of the motherboard limiting your chance of reconnecting the component back. When this happens, the system and the repair process might fail irreparably, except where you are able to trace the track supply line to that contact pad by digging deep into the motherboard. With mobile phone motherboards, it is difficult and in some cases impossible.

Figure 6.13: Retracing Broken Wiring Tracks on the PCB

Mainboard (Motherboard) Components and Layout

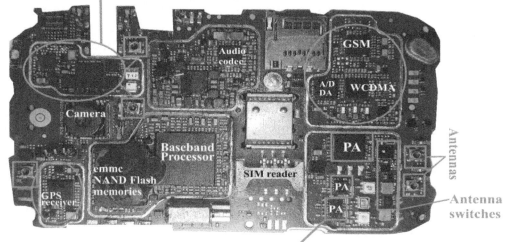

Figure 6.14: Smartphone PCB Layout

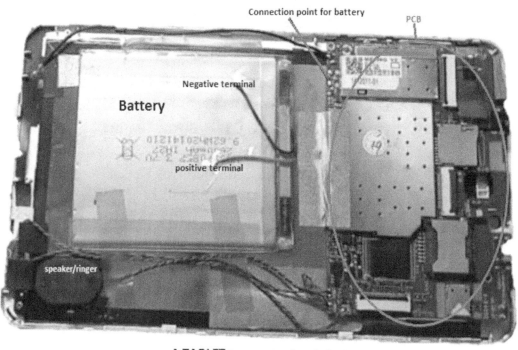

A TABLET (Screen overlays the entire front)

The first graphic image above captures the advancement from the foundational component layout design of mobile phones from the old 'Basic phone' generation (the 3310 Nokia example diagram in the first edition book) to the new 'smartphone' generation. The second image is that of a Tablet and comparatively, the only physical difference between a smartphone and a tablet is the size of the screen, which invariably determines the size of the mainboard (circuit board) or entire device.

Generally, a mobile device's circuit board is the heart of the system and contains a number of chips and discrete electronic components like resistors, capacitors, inductors etc. The motherboard buses (control, data or address bus for signal, data and memory addressing transport to and from the processor respectively) run through the printed copper wiring between the various components and System-on-Chips (SOC) modules, as well as the electrical wiring.

To understand the PCB layout design, one needs to first appreciate the functional description of the various function-specific integrated circuits along with their various inter-relationships with each other. It is totally a blind adventure to launch into the intricate design of mobile devices as a technician without a somewhat basic knowledge and understanding of the workings of the device's functional blocks.

Recent designs of smartphones follow the same foundational layout but with less number of discrete components, more powerful integrated circuits, multi-core processors or microcontrollers and device controllers.

In every mobile device, there are two distinct modules;

- The RF Module and
- The Baseband (BB) Module(Analog BB / Digital BB)

Before reviewing in brief the interoperation of the key functional components and modules, let us first describe and define them individually.

Key Components of the Radio Frequency (RF) Module

- Radio Frequency
- Power Amplifiers (PA)
- Low Noise Amplifiers (LNA)
- TxRx Switch (or Antenna Switch)
- SAW filters
- Local Oscillators (LO)
- Voltage Controlled Oscillators (VCO)
- RF Processor or Analog Baseband Processor

Key Components of the Baseband (BB) Module

- Analogue-To- Digital converter (AD/DA)
- Microprocessors
  [*Main Control Processor*
  Baseband Processor
  Digital Signal Processor (DSP)
  Application Processor]
- Power Control IC
- SIM or USIM card

Radio Frequency: RF is short for Radio Frequency. In communication engineering, the term "RF-signals" is used to denote signals containing information (voice, text or data, video etc) in the frequency bands used for radio communication.

Power Amplifiers (PA): It is usually located in the RF module within close proximity to the antenna of the mobile device and the Tx/Rx switch (or Antenna Switch). The PA acts as a band pass filter as well as amplifies message carrier signals for transmission on the network.

Low Noise Amplifiers (LNA): An amplifier usually increases the power of an input signal which consists of both a message signal and noise. Low Noise Amplifiers are used in the RF circuits to amplify very low-power signals without significantly degrading their signal-to-noise ratio. They are placed close to the Tx/Rx switch in the RF module so they filter noise from the incoming message signals before they are sent to the RF processor.

TxRx Switch (or Antenna Switch): The first point of interface by an incoming RF (Radio Frequency) signal after the receiving antenna is the Tx/Rx or antenna switch. There is a PCB wire track from the antenna to the Tx/Rx switch. The switch is a kind of frequency band selector. Remember that most mobile phones are multiple band phones from the GSM 850 Mhz, 900MHz, 1800 Mhz to 1900 Mhz bands extended to 2200MHz in smartphones. The TX/RX switch is normally open to two RX outlets (GSM_Rx and DCS_Rx. If it senses no control voltages at specific comparators, it will work as a duplexer (allowing bi-directional communication path over a single path) and the GSM900 signal is passed to GSM_Rx while GSM1800 signal is passed to DCS_Rx. In this duplexer mode the switch isolates the receiver and transmitter path even though they both share an antenna. The signal from GSM_Rx is then passed to the first of two or more Rx SAW filters.

SAW Filters: SAW is short for Surface Acoustic Wave. It is a type of mechanical wave motion which travels along the surface of a solid material. It has band pass filter characteristics whereby it provides out-of-band signal immunity. Their operation is based on the interference of mechanical surface waves. Input/output transducers are formed on a piezoelectric material through the conversion of electrical signals into mechanical waves and back due to the use of piezoelectric crystals in the SAW filters.

Local Oscillator: The Local Oscillator LO is an electronic device used to produce a sine wave or signal in the receiver which the RF signal processor mixes with the message signal to lower its frequency. This frequency conversion process produces separate differential (sum and difference) frequencies from the combined frequencies of the input signal and that of the local oscillator. This is what happens to the input signal from the SAW filters as they are sent for processing in the RF processor or receiver which in most cases comprises a mixer. The reduced frequency at this stage is usually called an Intermediate Frequency (IF).

On a general note, mobile phones do not have separate Receiver and Transmitter but Transceivers (a combined Transmitter/Receiver).

Voltage Controlled Oscillator (VCO): A voltage-controlled oscillator or VCO is an electronic oscillator whose oscillation frequency is controlled by a voltage input. The applied input voltage determines the instantaneous oscillation frequency. There is a feedback system known as Phased Locked Loop synthesizer which generates frequencies for both Rx and Tx in both frequency bands that synchronizes the VCO to the phase and frequency of an incoming signal.

The VCO generates very high frequencies in the range of 3420-3840 MHz whenever the Phased Locked Loop is in operation. These frequencies are divided by 2 or 4 in the RF processor so that they can generate all channels in GSM 900MHz-1800MHz. D.C voltages between 0.7 – 3.8V coming from the loop filter controls the VCO frequency. Even when the PLL is not operational, frequencies between 3 and 4GHz are still found at the VCO output.

RF Processor or Analog Baseband Processor (ABP): The RF Processors usually handle analogue radio frequency signal processing in the RF module. These signals are handed down from the RF front end. Most RF processors are transceivers (both a receiver and transmitter) with in-built IQ demodulators for signal modulation and demodulation.

The Analog Baseband part of a GSM modem is responsible for interface between the digital domain and the analog domain of the GSM modem. The Analog Baseband may consist of these integrated components in its IC package.

A/D and D/A section: Analog to Digital (A/D) and Digital to Analog (D/A) converters are responsible for digital to analog and analog to digital conversions.

The Control subsystem: The control subsystem acts as the controller of the input and output of any analog and digital signal.

The Charging Subsystem: A charging system is linked to the Analog Baseband which is responsible for charging mobile phone batteries.

Audio Codecs Section: Audio Codecs are responsible for the processing of analog and digital audio signals received through the microphone, speaker, headset, ringtones and the vibrator circuits. The signal output from its receiver circuitry is applied to its IQ demodulator. Here the data in the form of "In-phase" and "Quadrature" signal components are applied to the IQ demodulator and the raw data extracted for further processing by the phone.

In Smartphones, the Application Processor Core used is usually an Advanced RISC Machine (ARM) based processor which is specially optimized for application in minimal power consumption environments and are designed with the following assemblies;

a. The Processor Core
b. The Multimedia Modules
c. The Wireless Interfaces and
d. The Device Interfaces

The Multimedia modules are hardware implementation of one or more multimedia standards that perform multimedia related computations which are usually time consuming. Within this module are;

1. JPEG module for decoding pictures viewed on the display, and encoding pictures taken with the phone's camera.
2. MPEG module used for decoding streaming video, video on demand, and incoming video conferencing data as well as encoding video taken with the video camera.
3. Audio modules used for MP3 (music) players, or to encode and decode voice data.
4. Graphics Processing Unit (GPU) for rapidly manipulating multimedia functions. They accelerate image creation in frame buffers intended for output on a display unit. GPUs manage 2D and 3D graphics, video capture, playback, mobile gaming delivery and provide rich user interface.

Wireless Interfaces enable the smartphone to communicate with the cellular network and data network. The digital components of the Wireless Communication System are integrated into the chip as part of the application processor, while the analog section are placed off-chip as microcontrollers.

The following forms part of the wireless interface;

1. Bluetooth Module which enable communication with peripherals such as headset, and other nearby mobile devices.
2. Wi-Fi module which enable communication with local 802.11 networks.
3. GSM modules or modems which enable communication with the cellular network for both voice communication and internet access.

All three modules listed above are found as separate ICs on the PCB of mobile phones and tablets.

Device Interfaces enable mobile phones (smartphones or tablets) to communicate with peripheral devices such as display LCD, keypad, Universal Serial Bus (USB), Secure Digital card (SD), Multimedia Card (MMC), and camera. Each of these peripheral devices is connected to the application processor through a separate interface. For instance, the display controller interface allow for effective communication between the display and other modules integrated with SoC. Similarly camera interface allow for interaction between the camera and other digital modules while USB interface facilitates the connection of external devices through the USB port. SD/MMC interface enables smartphones to connect external memory storage devices.

In chapter 8 (Software Repairs) where a thorough understanding of the interplay between the processors, memories and storage is required, more explanations will be explored.

Chapter 7

Common Hardware Faults and Repair Procedures

The job description of a technician is to diagnose faults and carry out corrective repairs. Smartphones, Tablets, PDAs, and iPads just like every other electronic device or machine generally, might experience one failure or the other within their hardware during their lifecycle. In this chapter, we are going to learn some of the various common faults with smartphones and general repair procedures for effectively resolving such faults.

Every step or procedure described would be applicable to all mobile devices in the market today and perhaps in future. This is why this book and course has been designed to transfer skills and information in a way that equips the reader to act based upon knowledge and skills gained rather than enumerating quick-fix solution descriptions.

Mental Approach to Repairs

A technician is someone who studies, professes or practices technology according to dictionary definition (http:wiktionary.org). But to take it further, let's add that a technician is trained in the art of fault detection and correction through the application of hands-on practical skills in technology.

The purpose of this book is to provide training in mobile devices repair technology for mobile devices repair technicians. The mobile phone technician should possess an attitude of a solution provider who understands that EVERY faulty device brought in for repairs *was once a working system unit*. For any such device to be faulty, any one of the following causative factors listed below must have occurred.

Therefore, to correct the fault, the technician must think in line with the concept of 'cause *and effect*'.

Faults are introduced into a mobile device's system by any one of the following;

- Water or moisture
- Dust
- Wear and tear of Component parts
- Excessive heat to the system board
- Forceful impact on hard surfaces resulting in component removal or damage
- Short circuit within the system board (motherboard) wiring
- Open circuit within the system board (motherboard) wiring
- Voltage spikes during charging process
- Virus or Malware
- Corrupted Operating System software
- Incompatible third party applications
- System Settings user tampering or alteration
- And a host of other user related careless handling actions

Determining before-hand the possible cause(s) of a fault in the system either through interrogation of the client or technical intuition is an effective skill for speedy and efficient resolution of faults. Medical Doctors use this method too and it is important in any field of diagnostics to first try to determine the root cause(s) of any malfunction in a previously functional system.

Components' Terminals or Contact points

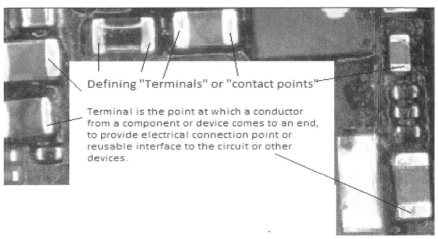

Defining "Terminals" or "contact points"

Terminal is the point at which a conductor from a component or device comes to an end, to provide electrical connection point or reusable interface to the circuit or other devices.

Common Hot-Swappable Faults

- **Power-On Failure**: When a mobile device fails to Switch-On, it is referred to as a 'dead' phone situation.
- **Automatic Power- Off and Restart Fault**: The mobile device switches off automatically without the user initiating it, during/after a call or the mobile device just reboots itself.
- **Microphone Failure**: When calls by a user to other users are successful but the other end cannot hear any sound while the user can hear them.
- **Speaker Failure**: When calls by a user to other users are successful but the user cannot hear a sound from the other end while being heard at the other end.
- **Ringer Failure**: When calls to a mobile device user produces no alert sound or ring tone.
- **Display Faults**: The mobile device's LCD is physically seen to be broken, shows ink blots or shows no graphics or the touchscreen is non-responsive.
- **Touchscreen Failure**: When the Touchscreen input system fails to function.
- **Vibrator Failure**: When calls to the mobile device produces no alert vibration when vibrator alert option is set to "ON" in the device's settings.
- **Charging Faults**: Failure in charging the device's battery and it manifests in several forms.
- **Fast Battery Drain Fault**: The device's battery gets fully charged but also gets drained very quickly.
- **Network Problem**: When there is no network signal in the phone or poor network signal (limited network). It manifests in various ways.
- **SIM Card Faults**: When the SIM card fails to be recognized by the mobile device.
- **Hanging/ Freezing Faults**: The mobile device freezes frequently interrupting user operations and sometimes followed by a restart/reboot.
- **Automatic Call-Drop Faults**: When calls to or from the device gets disconnected intermittently.
- **Bluetooth Failure**: When the device's Bluetooth does not function.

- **Camera Failure**: When the device's camera fails to function.
- **Radio Functionality Failure**: When the FM Radio does not function for devices with such features.
- **Memory Card Reader Faults**: When the device fails to detect memory cards.
- **Internet Connectivity Failure**: When the mobile device cannot gain access to the internet or Wi-Fi access but can initiate and receive calls.
- **Incomplete Power-On Failure**: This is when a device switches ON but freezes on the appearance of the brand logo or a blank display.
- **Hands-free Jack Faults**: When the external earphone connection to the mobile device is not functioning or leads to the failure of the entire audio system.

The list above is not an exhaustive one as faulty smartphones usually exhibit various other vague mutations or combinations of the above-listed common faults. However, no matter the nature of the fault or combination of faulty behavior exhibited by a mobile device, be confident enough to first dismantle the device and gain access to the motherboard. All brands and models of smartphones and tablets in the market today or in the future are basically electronic devices. The technical knowledge gained in this book would be applicable to all. The general structure of all mobile device systems and components are similar, only differentiated by the various manufacturers' brand names.

Repair Guidelines for Various Common Faults

Power-On failure

Every device must first be powered-On (switched-On) before its functions or purpose can be utilized. When the device fails to switch-On, it is what is commonly called 'dead phone' in local parlance to mean that the client brought the device in an unresponsive state.

"Dead phone" actually means that the phone could not receive electric current or control signal when the power switch is pressed or the CPU-watchdog "disable pin" is grounded. Specifically, in smartphones and tablets it could result from damage of the Master Boot Record partition of the ROM, corruption of the boot file in eMMC or NAND, or the File System (Operating System). Also, nominal supply voltage to the phone is usually between 3.6V and 4.2V (Vbatt voltage); if it is below 3.1v, the phone is prevented by the power IC from powering up.

In summary, a "Dead phone" situation could result from any of the following causes;

A. Dead battery.

B. Corrupted initialization/boot sector files due to virus or improper usage.

C. Damaged Operating System software.

D. Failed Power switch.

E. Damaged battery terminals.

F. Water or moisture on the motherboard.

G. Open circuit or short circuiting of motherboard components.

H. Damaged Power IC or Microprocessor chip (CPU).

Testing, Troubleshooting & Repair Procedures

To begin the process of repairing a dead smartphone or tablet, carry out the following investigations or actions;

i.   Let us assume you have an uncluttered work bench, with your set of precision screw drivers, cleaning solution like IPA or ultrasonic cleaner, brush, digital multi-meter, soldering-iron /station and computer system with software repair tools.

ii.   Firstly, disassemble the device.

iii.   Remove the device's battery and test for voltage with your digital multi-meter. Expected voltage range is between 3.6V and 3.8V D.C or 4.2V max for some models. If it meets the expected range, then battery is ruled out as the cause. However, if the battery voltage is 3.1V or below, the mobile device cannot power-on.

iv.   Next, test with a fully charged similar battery of the same model of the device and try to power ON the device. If successful, then the client's battery is the cause of the failure. Boost the battery voltage if normal charging with a charger fails to shoot up the battery voltage.

v.   But if there is no success even with a good battery, connect the device to the computer, run the mobile repair software application and check if the software can read data from the device.

Note: Not all mobile repair software applications have this feature. While it is the requisite standard procedure, if you do not have the software tools for the device or the software application does not have this feature to check communication with the device you may skip this step.

The problem with skipping this step is that most times, technicians who focus only on hardware repair procedures neglect the fact that the problem might be software related, and then go to extreme measures fiddling with the hardware to the extent of damage to the motherboard chips (ICs). When as a last resort they later try software repair or the client eventually takes the device to a software equipped technician, the Microprocessor or Flash chip may have been damaged by their actions thereby denying the client the possibility of a successful resuscitation of their device unknowingly. Therefore, if you skip this step for any reason, be tactfully careful when working or carrying out any repair procedure on the hardware ICs in order not to cause irreparable damage.

vi. If there is communication with the device through software, it is not also a guarantee that formatting the boot sector or a full flash programming will resuscitate the device. It however confirms that both the power IC and Microprocessor are in good condition. The software process may run successfully but yet the device remains unresponsive to the power-On switch. While that is a good first step before returning to hardware checks, the disadvantage of 'full flashing' is to the client. If the final solution lies in correcting a hardware failure, formatting or flashing the device would have resulted in the loss of important data from the device by that operation although in most cases, restoring the device back to operation may be of paramount concern to the technician and maybe, the client.

vii. Make a decision between flashing the device immediately and carrying out further basic hardware checks.

viii. Activate three of your five senses and be alert when dismantling any device - the sense of sight (for keen observation looking out for components that may fall out from the device or missing components from any termination point, any charred part of the device motherboard for burnt components, water or other liquid spill, dirty or rusty PCB or any form of technical abnormality), the sense of smell (for burnt out part odor), sense of feeling (for excessively hot components/ICs).

ix. Carry out a thorough cleaning service on the motherboard. Be sure to remove sensitive peripheral components attached to the motherboard interfaces like camera, the LCD, microphones, speakers etc. Clean their contact point connectors and sockets too. Do this manually or using an ultrasonic cleaner. Also ensure that the cleaning solution flows into the underside of the ICs to wash out any foreign particles underneath.

x. Dry the motherboard completely. IPA (Isopropyl Alcohol) and other recommended electronic board cleaning solvents dry as quickly as you apply them without leaving any residual oily deposits. Sunlight will take a very long time while an ultrasonic cleaner, hair drier or the blower from your hot air soldering station can dry the motherboard very quickly.

xi.　After drying the board, connect the LCD and battery and attempt power-On again. There should be success in most cases where the cause of failure is due to a liquid spill or moisture on the motherboard. Water causes oxidation which is corrosion or the degradation of metals. Resistance between the circuits drop due to the shorting (short-circuit connections whereby component's leads that are not by design meant to be joined together are joined together bridging the positive and negative supply lines) of terminals from rust deposits on deteriorating solder joints.

xii.　If the phone does not power-On, check the power switch. There are various types of switches used in mobile devices. Read the section on repairing switch faults for details.

xiii.　If the Power-On switch is ok, check the battery terminals by re-soldering its base contacts or ribbon cabling connected to the motherboard. Using your multi-meter for continuity or resistance test, check that the positive and negative terminals (VBat+ and VBat-) are not shorted. Check also that the BSI (Battery Status Indicator) line is not short-circuited to either of the terminals. Check the continuity between the battery connector pins that make contact with the battery and its base on the motherboard.

xiv.　Attempt power-On if all the above tests are ok. If no success, carry out a general hot air re-soldering process at moderate temperatures across the entire motherboard. This will reconnect surface mounted electronic components whose lead terminals may have deteriorated and which perhaps created open circuit connections in the circuit board.

xv.　If there is no success too, specific re-hot procedure described in details in the section "Soldering" is carried out on two major ICs; the power IC first and if there is no success, the Microprocessor IC secondly. You do not need to carry out this step if you confirmed the status of these two ICs with software check in step IV above.

xvi.　If these procedures fail, and having effectively worked on the processor chip and power IC, you may retry the use of software. This is because an initial trial with software as described in step (iv) may not have succeeded with the device communicating with the software and the computer. When that happens, step (xv) is usually carried out as any failure with those specific motherboard system chips will result in the inability of the software repair procedure succeeding. So at this juncture, carry out Flash Programming on the device with the relevant software repair tools.

xvii. If there is no success yet, IC BGA re-ball procedure should be carried out for either the power IC, Microprocessor or any other IC in cases where there is an IC that is observed to be overheating. This is the case also if the motherboard has a history of water or liquid spillage as either observed by the technician or revealed by the user client.

xviii. Should this fail after an attempt to power-On the device, then the internal wiring of the motherboard may have short-circuited or open circuited. This will require a critical study of the circuit-board diagram. Read the section "PCB/Motherboard Faults" for details on removing short circuit.

How to Boost a Battery

When a mobile device's battery is low, it requires normal charging to raise the voltage. However, when the battery voltage is almost or completely depleted with the voltage ranging between 0 to 2.0V DC, a normal charging process using the recommended charger might not bring the battery up to nominal rating of 3.6V to power the device. Certain conditions like cold weather conditions may affect the behavior of a battery. When this happens, a user might report a "dead phone" or "no charging" fault condition. To boost the battery, take either of the following simple steps;

1. Use a battery booster machine sold in the market OR
2. Use any charger adapter that is functioning but no longer in use. They all have a DC output of about 5.0V. Cut out the charging pin and expose the positive and negative flexible cords within the outer PVC covering. Several color combinations are usually used to denote positive and negative polarity;

a. Black is usually for negative if combined with red which is positive.

b. Black is negative if combined with white streaked with black stripes which is positive.

c. Blue is negative if combined with either red or white which is for positive.

d. Brown is negative if combined with either red or white as positive.

If in doubt about the color combinations and polarity, use your multi-meter to check. Plug the adapter into a wall socket outlet. With the probes on each of the wires, expect a positive value if the polarity matches with the red and black probes touching each wire. If the polarity is reversed, a negative value of DC voltage will be displayed. Be sure the adapter output ranges between 5V-5.5V DC.

Having determined the positive (+) and (-) wire from the charger adapter, identify the positive (+) and (-) battery pins as well. On the battery body, it is usually marked.

You can also determine with your multi-meter the same way you did for the adapter wires. Once that is settled, plug the charger adapter to a live wall socket outlet, connect;

Positive adapter wire **to** *Positive battery pin*
Negative *adapter wire* **to Negative** *battery pin*

Hold this in place for about 10 to 15 minutes. If the charge on the battery reaches about 3.5V DC, then use the normal recommended charger to charge through the device. At 3.5V, the battery can power the device but will display "low battery".

Repairing Faulty Charging Circuits

Charging Systems are used for restoring charge voltage to batteries which are the primary source of power to smartphones or tablets. The charging system comprises of the following components;

- The External Charging Adapter
- The Internal Charging Port
- The Motherboard Charging Sub-circuit
- The Battery

Each of these component units can fail to function resulting into a user client complaint of a failed charging process. The mobile device might fail to charge its battery due to any of the following reasons;

A. The external charging adapter has completely malfunctioned

B. The contact pins in the charger's cable connector has broken, bent or lost connection with its electrical supply cords from the adapter.

C. The charger's D.C output supply to the mobile device is either below 5V D.C. or above 5V D.C.

D. The contact pins in the charging system port on the motherboard has broken, bent or lost contact with the motherboard.

E. The internal motherboard charging sub-circuit has one or more malfunctioning electronic components either as open circuit or short circuit or damaged due to water or moisture on the motherboard.

F. The battery could be damaged, empty or dead.

Testing, Troubleshooting & Repair Procedures

To begin the process of repairing a charging fault, carry out the following investigations and actions if the charging unit is not swappable but on-board;

i. First, you need to connect the phone to a charger; connect to a live power supply socket and observe the behavior of the mobile device.

ii. The next thing to do is to connect another functional charging adapter that is compatible with that particular mobile device to confirm if the fault is from the client's charging adapter. In some cases, this basic confirmation may have been done already by the client but it is still safe to do so. If it happens to be the case, advise the client to buy a recommended charging adapter. Let me add that if your service center is engaged in sales, this presents opportunity to profit from sales.

iii. If charging adapter is not the problem, check the battery. Make sure the battery is a healthy one. If the problem is the battery, change it.

iv. If battery is not the problem, turn OFF and disassemble the mobile device to gain access to the charging port. Ensure that the pins are in good condition within their respective housing assemblies.

v. If the external facing pin or pins that mate with the charger cable are in good shape, check the inner motherboard contact pins and ensure none is bent, broken or detached from the motherboard. In the case of detachment from the PCB, visual inspection is hardly enough because they are very tiny and the solder underneath each pin may deteriorate without being visible.

vi.   If the charging port is damaged, replace by de-soldering and re-soldering a new one. They are sold in phone parts shops. Some ports are not soldered to the PCB but connected with ribbon cables. Most smartphones have detachable charging sub-circuit boards that are not soldered to the motherboard. These are easier to replace than repair. An example is the Samsung Galaxy series beginning from Galaxy S4.

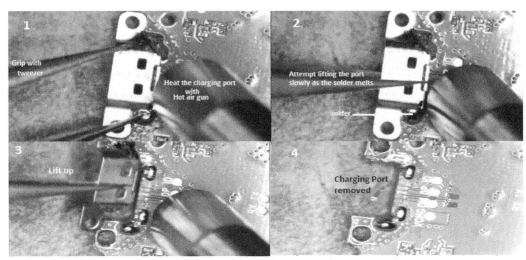

Process for the Removal of a Charging port

vii.   Use PCB cleaner to clean the charging port contacts thoroughly before changing the port.

viii.   Switch ON the soldering station and using a blower, run hot air on the charging port connection pins. In the absence of a rework station, use a sharp tip soldering iron to re-solder each pin one after the other. Do not add extra soldering lead to the terminals. This will muddy up and bridge the terminals. Instead rub a very slight quantity of flux on the pins before heating.

Caution: *Excessive heating and movement of soldering iron on a contact point especially when flux is applied may damage the motherboard contact pad that links the internal PCB wiring to connect with surface components.*

ix.   Test the device by connecting the battery and a charger to it. Confirm whether it is okay. If the problem persists, next...

x.   Check the fuse. There is usually a fuse. (See section "Charging Circuits" in *Chapter 3: Basic Electronics and Circuit Analysis*. Carry out a continuity test, also taught in the previous book. If there is no buzzer sound, change or bridge with a strand of flexible wire. If there is a buzzer sound, it is fine. Continue electrical level troubleshooting with a multi-meter to check and replace discrete electronic components such as Zener diode regulator or transistor etc. or repairing motherboard ICs (in this case charging IC). Apply the knowledge gained in *Chapter 6: Electronics Fundamentals* and the section "IC BGA soldering and Repair" in chapter four of the book "*Mobile Phones and Tablets Repairs: A Complete Guide for Beginners and Professionals*".

xi.   As shown in the image below, recent designs have swappable charging units with other peripheral components like ringers attached, connected to the PCB through flexible connectors. This makes it easier to replace without a soldering process. Simply replace with a new unit if it can't be repaired. See figure 7.1 below.

Fig. 7.1: Charging port module

To carry out a simple charging circuit trace, follow the guidelines below. The USB charging ports usually have four pins. From the front-facing plug-in direction, the positive (+) pin is on the extreme left while the negative (-) pin is on the extreme right side.

After disassembling the phone, looking at the port from the inside of the mainboard like in the image below, the polarity position will change with the positive charging port pin on the right while the negative pin will be on the left from the inside view angle. Usually at close proximity to the charging port are collocated discrete electronic control components (capacitors, resistors, diode etc.). In a real PCB they will appear like below;

Discrete electronic components

To trace the circuit, start by locating and checking the fuse. A fuse is a low value resistor, usually about 1KΩ. It serves to protect circuits against hazardous current overload by blowing up (open circuiting) and disconnecting the circuit from the overcurrent source.

i. Using a multi-meter, select continuity diode test or resistance test and check the fuse for continuity. It will produce a beep (continuous) if it is unbroken (in good condition) and no beep if it has become broken or open circuited. A continuous state would read zero Ohms

ii. Place one probe of the multi-meter on the positive pin of the charging port and trace by touching the second probe on each edge terminal of the discrete components. The fuse is usually black like other resistors on the PCB or colored (sky-blue, milky-white or other unusual color different from most other components on the PCB).

iii. Any indication of continuity (beep) by the second probe touching both sides (edge terminals) of a resistor indicates a working fuse. You will identify a faulty fuse if the trace from the first probe on the positive pin to one edge terminal of a resistor is continuous while touching the other edge terminal of the same resistor produces no beep.

iv. If however the fuse tests 'OK', check the status of the Zener diode, capacitors or transistors as the case may be. If they all test 'OK', identify the glass charging control chip and re-hot. If re-hot fails, replace the chip.

xii. Also, test for voltage output from the charging port to determine if it needs to be changed. Plug the charger into the charging port and test the input voltage coming into the port. It should be ±5 - 5.5V d.c. Turn the multi-meter's dial selector switch to 20V d.c block. Place the positive probe on the positive right pin and the negative probe on the ground pin (negative pin). Note that the body of the charging port and any metal part of components can act as ground point.

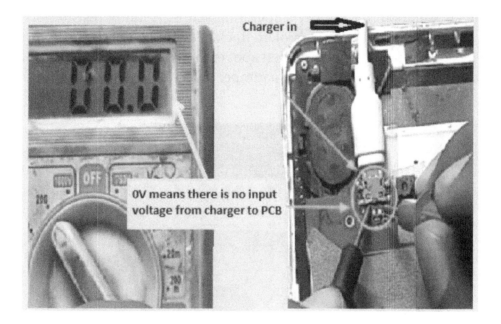

Faulty Charging Error Notifications

    a. Charging paused Battery temp too low (Samsung)
    b. Charging paused Battery temp too high (Samsung)
    c. 'X' Stop charging
    d. Charging error stop charging
    e. Self-charging Mobile Phone
    f. Phone only charge with PC and not chargers

Tips

1. Download the PCB diagram for each phone under repair and trace the circuit using your multi-meter.

2. Use the internet library through Google images to search for each specific device's pictorial cable-section (PCB wiring track) traced by other professionals who have studied the circuit diagram of the phone.

3. Buy, activate and use the Easy Draw software

"Not Charging": When a phone displays "Not Charging" as soon as a charger is plugged in, it means it wouldn't charge the battery despite sensing a charging voltage. This problem occurs when a required current or voltage is not enough to boost up and charge the phone's battery. One reason for this problem is a faulty BSI Line (Battery Status Indicator) that tells the charging control circuit about the battery's operating status. A faulty resistor, capacitor, voltage regulator or broken track also can be the cause. If you have done basic repair procedure as listed above, then carry out a PCB trace to either replace a component or use a jumper cable to correct an open circuit.

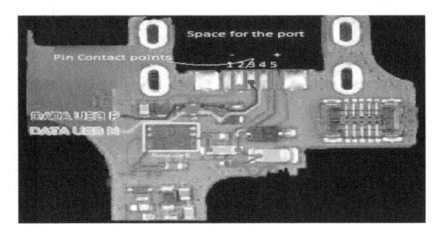

Figure 7.2a: Sample Jumper tracks for LG L80 USB Charging Problem

The image above is an illustration (though it should work for the particular model indicated) of how the internet can be helpful in providing images contributed by other technicians. Where there is no Easy Draw software yet, or access to schematic diagrams for a particular model, leveraging the internet search engines can produce results like this one above which can be leveraged. Also, when by applying the troubleshooting steps learnt in this book you discover solutions, you can as well enrich the community by sharing.

"Charger Not Supported": when you encounter this fault, after the basic general steps above has been exhausted, apply same as in 'Not Charging' above.

Charger Not Supported problem is caused by a faulty BTEMP thermistor component or broken track. BTEMP stands for Battery Temperature. It is a battery pin used to monitor the battery temperature status during charging. In most devices, a resistor (a 47Kilo Ohm resistor which becomes open-circuited due to water damaged or other causes) causes this charging fault. The solution is to find it and remove or replaced it.

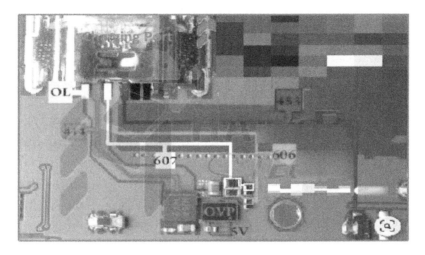

Figure 7.2b: Samsung Galaxy J6 charging Circuit Track

"Charging paused Battery temp too low or high": when a mobile device displays something similar to the image below;

Figure 7.2c

Caution/Disclaimer: *These example images are only meant to show the reader what is obtainable when accessed through online searches. The solutions shown are not being endorsed by this book due to this posting here. This type of image differs for each product model. Using images sourced online are at the technician's discretion!*

In many situations with tablets and smartphones, charging issues can actually be software related. If the phone's charger is in good condition while the phone heats up at regular intervals even when at rest, it might be due to heavy application usage or malware activity in the background. Smartphones and tablets have certain ICs or component units that dissipate more heat during multiple application processing. Such chips include;

a. The processor - when an application that utilizes heavy CPU processing is running.
b. The Graphics Processing Unit, GPU- when your app uses OpenGL.
c. The display when lit over a long time (depending also on the brightness setting).
d. The battery (when charged continuously or drained quickly).
e. The modem also needs much power for 3G/4G/LTE data transfers.

There is a safety mechanism built into mobile devices to monitor battery temperatures through the BTemp battery connector pins. This safety mechanism will react with this type of charging error notification for high battery temperatures when these components get excessively hot. In most cases, it is likely a combination of all the above listed chips causing the problem. Corrupted applications can also cause overheating in which case you have to uninstall such applications. When in doubt about which application could be the culprit, a hard reset of the device or software flash programming becomes an option. Take the following initial steps before attempting hardware repair;

i. Lower the screen brightness.
ii. Uninstall any third party App that may have been recently downloaded into the device.
iii. Switch to 3G only in the mobile networks settings: Go to Settings>Wireless & Networks>More>Mobile Networks>Use only 3G networks (saves battery juice). This is because when a mobile device is in an area where 4G network (or the higher Generation Network technology) is absent; the radio will consistently be searching, overworking the modem and thereby generating heat.
iv. If all else fails including hardware repair steps, Use software repair procedures as covered in Software Repairs section of this book.

For electrical and electronic level repairs, use the earlier stated guidelines to apply hardware wiring track-tracing, whereby we identify points where PCB wiring has opened and need to be bypassed with jumper cabling for current to flow to the right discrete electronic components. See track trace jumper samples below.

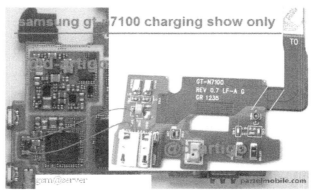

Credit: Google Images from http://forum.gsmhosting.com

Figure 7.2d

"Charging paused Battery temp too high":

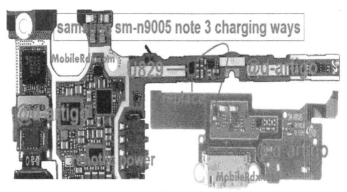

Credit: Google Images from http://forum.gsmhosting.com

Figure 7.2e

Automatic "Self-charging" Fault: When a mobile device behaves this way, it is symptomatic of a loopback current from the phone's battery to the charging circuit or IC. A simple solution is to clean the charging port contacts and the entire PCB thoroughly because a short-circuit condition is existing. However, if it does not solve the problem, in which case the short-circuit condition is not existing on the PCB surface mount; next thing to do is to carry out a PCB trace (troubleshooting) to find the faulty capacitor or charge sensor chip.

Audio and Alert Faults

The audio systems present in mobile devices consist of the Microphone system, the Speaker, the Ringer, and the external Hands- free jack. We shall be discussing about each system one after the other.

Speaker Faults

The speaker or earpiece is the device responsible for hearing audio or voice communications during a phone call. When they become faulty, it is signified by the following behaviors;

- The user of the mobile device will not hear from the other end of the conversation completely.
- The user can barely hear the caller's voice from the other end.
- The voice signal from the other end will be cranky, stifled by noisy interference.

Testing, Troubleshooting & Repair Procedure

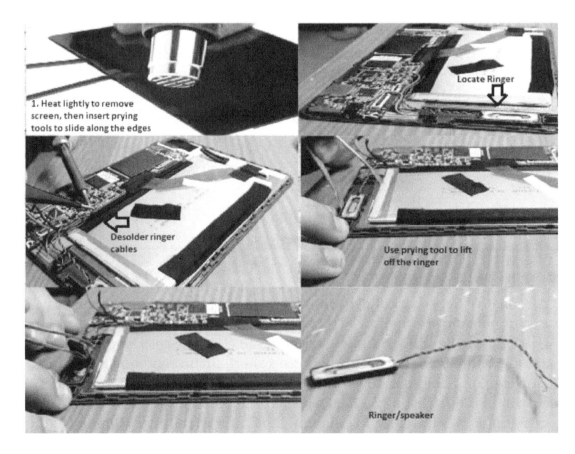

To repair speaker faults, follow the steps below;

i. First of all, confirm the behavior of the mobile device by initiating a call. If you do not want to make a complete call, make a toll-free subscriber support call to your service provider as applicable in your home country and listen. Once the call connects and is active, increase the side volume-up button. For phones without side volume keys, check the home central four-directional key (for left, right, up, down cursor directions) and press the right or up keys. Whichever one is for volume-up, a slider will pop up on the LCD display indicating an increment.

If the slider is already at maximum and no audio from the other side, then the fault is within the system.

ii. Next, turn OFF and disassemble the mobile device.

iii. Locate the speaker and detach or disconnect it from the motherboard.

iv. Observe the PCB contact pads where the speaker contacts connect to (2 pins or cords for positive [+] and negative [-] electrical supply) for dirt, oxidation or corrosion. Where it is soldered, check for breaks, rust or oxidation and re-solder the contacts.

v. Clean the PCB contact pads thoroughly whether you observed the presence of dirt, oxidation, and corrosion or not (where the speaker terminals are not soldered to the PCB).

vi. Use your multi-meter to take readings from the speaker. Resistance values for a good one ranges between 30~33Ω ±3. If the speaker also serves as a ringer (dual function), the value is between 7-8Ω.

vii. Connect back the speaker if the values are good or replace with an alternate good one and test. If okay, end of repairs.

viii. If it is not okay, use cleaning fluid and brush; thoroughly clean the entire motherboard with focus on the electronic components surrounding the speaker contact pads' vicinity. Most times by design, the control components are directly on the reverse side of the PCB parallel to the same spot where the speaker or peripheral component being controlled is connected. This helps to remove any surface short-circuit agent like rust between surface mounted components.

ix. Then, turn ON the rework station and run a moderate temperature hot air stream on the PCB with focus on electronic elements around the speaker vicinity which control current to the speaker. This is to correct open-circuit connections for deteriorated solder joints between the components and the motherboard.

x.   Test the speaker again by powering ON the device and initiating a call. If okay, end of repairs. But if it is still not okay, power ON the motherboard and test for the presence of voltage at the contact pads for the speaker. Begin components and motherboard IC (in this case audio IC) troubleshooting and repair procedures as learned in *Chapter 3: Basic Electronics and Circuits Analysis* and the section "IC BGA Soldering and Repair" in chapter six of this book.

Microphone Faults

The Microphone or mouth-piece is the device responsible for transmitting voice sounds to the other end during a phone call. When they become faulty, the following behaviors are observed;

- The user of the mobile device will hear audible voice from the other end of the communication but cannot be heard on the other side.
- The user can barely be heard by the caller on the other end.
- The voice signal transmitted to the other end will be cranky, stifled by noisy interference.

Testing, Troubleshooting & Repair Procedure

To repair Microphone or Mic or Mouth-piece faults, follow the steps below;

i.   First of all, confirm the behavior of the mobile device by initiating a call. If the user at the other end cannot hear you while you can hear the voice, then there is a problem.

ii.   Next, turn OFF and disassemble the mobile device.

iii. Locate the Microphone and detach or disconnect it from the motherboard.

iv.   Observe the PCB contact pads for the Microphone contacts (2 pins or cords for positive [+] and negative [-] electrical supply) to check for moulds, dirt, oxidation or corrosion.

v.   Clean the PCB contact pads thoroughly whether you observed the presence of dirt, oxidation or corrosion or not.

vi.   Use your multi-meter to take readings from the Microphone (Mic or mouth-piece). Resistance values for a good one ranges between 700~1700Ω ±100. Reading is taken only with [+ve] probe to [+ve] terminal of Mic and [–ve] probe to [–ve] terminal of Mic and not the reverse.

vii. Connect back the Microphone if the values are good or replace with an alternate good one and test. If it is okay, end of repairs.

viii. If it is still not okay, use cleaning fluid with brush and thoroughly clean the entire motherboard with focus on the electronic components around the microphone contact pads' vicinity. Most times by design the control components are placed directly on the reverse side of the PCB, parallel to the same spot as the Mic or the peripheral component being controlled. This helps to remove any surface short-circuit agent like rust between surface mounted components.

ix.   Then turn ON the rework station and run a moderate temperature hot air stream on the PCB with focus on control electronic elements around the Mic's vicinity. This is to correct open-circuit connections for deteriorated solder joints between the components and the motherboard.

x.   Test the Microphone again by powering ON the device and initiating a call. If it tested okay, end of repairs.

xi.   If it is not yet okay, power ON the motherboard and test for the presence of voltage at the PCB contact pads for the Microphone. Begin components and motherboard IC (in this case audio IC) troubleshooting and repair procedures as learned in *Chapter 3: Basic Electronics and Circuits Analysis* and the section "IC BGA Soldering and Repair" in chapter six of this book.

Ringer Faults

The ringer or loudspeaker is the device responsible for caller alert, music and other notifications to a user. When they become faulty, it is signified by the following behaviors;

- The user of the mobile device will not hear the ringtone when called by another mobile device user or telephone.

- The device rings but the user can barely hear the sound even while with the phone or other multimedia and notification sounds are very low.

- The sound from the phone will be crackling, very low, like a damaged loudspeaker.

Testing, Troubleshooting & Repair Action Steps

To repair ringer or buzzer faults, follow the procedure below;

i. First of all confirm the behavior of the mobile device by initiating a call to the device from another phone or check the phone's Settings>Sound>Alert Type>Volume. The volume should be high enough and the alert type option should not be 'silent' or 'vibrate only'. If the settings are ok...

ii. Next, turn OFF and disassemble the mobile device.

iii. Locate the ringer and detach or disconnect it from the motherboard.

iv. Observe the PCB contact pads for the ringer contacts (2 pins or cords for positive [+] and negative [-] electrical supply) for dirt, oxidation or corrosion.

v. Clean the PCB contact pads thoroughly whether you observe the presence of dirt, oxidation or corrosion or not.

vi. Use your multi-meter to take readings from the ringer. Resistance values for a good one ranges between 8~10Ω ±1. Older monotonic ringers read between 15-18Ω. Don't worry if you hear the continuity beep sound.

vii. Connect back the ringer if the values are good or replace with an alternate good one and test. If ok, end.

viii. If it is not ok, use cleaning fluid and brush and thoroughly clean the entire motherboard with focus on the electronic components surrounding the speaker contact pads' vicinity. Most times by design, the control components are directly on the reverse side of the PCB parallel to the same spot with the speaker or peripheral component being controlled. This helps to remove any surface short-circuit agent like rust between surface mounted components.

ix. Then turn ON the rework station and run a moderate temperature stream of hot air on the PCB with focus on control electronic elements around the speaker vicinity. This is to correct open-circuit connections for deteriorated solder joints between the components and the motherboard.

x. Test the ringer again by powering ON the device. If ok, end.

xii. If it is still not ok, power ON the motherboard and test for the presence of voltage at the contact pads for the ringer. Begin components and motherboard IC (in this case Audio IC) troubleshooting and repair procedures as learned in *Chapter 3: Basic Electronics and Circuits Analysis* and the section "IC BGA Soldering and Repair" in chapter six of this book.

Vibrator Faults

Vibrators provide silent alert notifications. They rarely develop faults although just about any device can fail. Inside a vibrator is a control unit which has a small DC motor that drives a gear. Attached to the gear, there is a small weight mounted off-the-center on the gear. When the motor spins, the gear/weight combination spins at 100 to 150 RPM, the off-center mounting causing a strong vibration.

Testing, Troubleshooting & Repair Procedure

Follow the following steps to repair a vibrator failure.

i. First of all confirm the behavior of the mobile device by initiating a call to the device from another phone or check the phone's Settings>Sound>Alert Type>Vibrate & Ring or Vibrate Only'. If the settings are okay but the phone does not still vibrate, then (ii)

ii. Next, turn OFF and disassemble the mobile device.

iii. Locate the vibrator and detach or disconnect it from the motherboard.

iv. Observe the PCB contact pads for the vibrator contacts (2 pins or cords for positive [+] and negative [-] electrical supply) and look out for dirt, oxidation or corrosion.

v. Clean the PCB contact pads thoroughly whether you observe the presence of dirt, oxidation or corrosion or not.

vi.   Use the multi-meter to take readings from the vibrator. Resistance values for a good one ranges between 8~16Ω ±1.

vii.   Connect back the vibrator if the values are good or replace with an alternate good one and test. If it is okay, end of repairs.

viii.   If it is not okay, use cleaning fluid and brush and thoroughly clean the entire motherboard with focus on the electronic components surrounding the vibrator contact pads vicinity. Most times by design the control components are directly on the reverse side of the PCB parallel to the same spot on which the vibrator or peripheral component being controlled is mounted. This helps to remove any surface short-circuit agent like rust between surface mounted components.

ix.   Then, turn ON the rework station and run a moderate temperature hot air stream on the PCB with focus on control electronic elements around the speaker vicinity. This is to correct open-circuit connections for deteriorated solder joints between the components and the motherboard.

x.   Test the vibrator again by powering ON the device. If okay, end repairs.

xiii.   If it is still not okay, power ON the motherboard and test for the presence of voltage at the PCB contact pads for the vibrator. Begin components and motherboard IC troubleshooting and repair procedures as learned in *Chapter 3: Basic Electronics and Circuits Analysis* and the section "IC BGA Soldering and Repair" in chapter six of this book.

Video/Graphics/Display faults

The visual output unit of mobile phones is the LCD (Liquid Crystal Display). LCDs get damaged in a number of ways ranging from the following;

- LCD Glass (screen) breakage.
- Ink blots covering the entire screen.
- No visual elements (dark screen or blank lit screen).
- Presence of visual elements without background LED lighting.
- Part or whole of the Touchscreen not responding to input.

LCDs like almost all the peripheral components of the mobile phone motherboard are field replaceable units. This means that the unit should be replaced completely when they develop a fault instead of attempting to repair them.

This does not eliminate the possibility of technical improvisation. Display faults could be caused by any of the following;

    a. Mobile device impact on hard surfaces.

    b. Water or other liquid damage.

Testing, Troubleshooting & Repair Action Steps

The following action steps should be taken for a faulty display unit.

    i.   Determine first and foremost that the mobile device can transmit and receive calls. Although in some cases, as a result of the screen's blind status, the device's power-ON routine might not be completed especially if a user input is required like a "Yes" or "No" pop-up menu option.

    ii.   Next step is to Turn OFF and dismantle the mobile device.

    iii.   Disconnect the LCD unit from the motherboard if it is not permanently soldered to the motherboard.

    iv.   For LCDs with fused flex connectors; with their ribbon cable tips (socket-end) permanently soldered on the PCB, clean the contacts and re-solder its multiple pin contacts to the PCB (re-flow the solder). If the LCD has a detachable socket or clip on the PCB, clean both the flexible connector's socket-end pins and the PCB socket pins. Re-solder with soldering iron one pin after the other. Use of hot air stream from the blower should be avoided because the heat will melt the plastics housing the contact pins.

    v.   For LCDs with separate detachable flex connectors, both ends of the flex connector (LCD-end socket and PCB-end socket) should be cleaned to remove dirt, oxidation or corrosion. Then reflow the solder under the pins using soldering iron one after the other.

    vi.   Clean the entire PCB focusing on the Display unit area.

    vii.   Reconnect the LCD unit and test. If okay, end of repairs.

    viii.   If it is not okay, change the LCD flex with a new one. If okay, end of repairs.

ix.   If it is not okay, change the LCD and connect with old flex connector. If okay, end of repairs.

x.   If it is still not okay, change both the LCD and its flex connector. If okay, then both are faulty simultaneously. This is often the case with fused LCD and flex scenario but rare when the flex connector and LCD are separable.

xi.   If change of the entire LCD assembly does not solve the problem, and either the old LCD and Flex or the new ones are confirmed to be in good condition, then the investigation shifts to the PCB. The entire display system could fail too - LCD, flex, flex socket or jack, PCB control components (electronics and display IC) and this occurs when there is liquid damage.

xi.   Then check the socket on the PCB where the screen's flexible connector is plugged into. Firstly, re-solder the pins of this connection jack one after the other. Do NOT run hot air to avoid melting its plastic property.

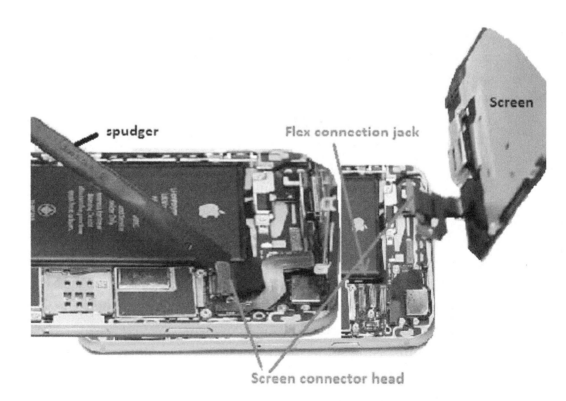

xii.   If the fault persists, begin an electrical track trace between the socket and the surrounding discrete electronic components. Apply the motherboard electrical level troubleshooting steps learnt in *Chapter 6: Electronics Fundamentals* of the first edition book "*Mobile Phones and Tablets Repairs: A Complete Guide for Beginners and Professionals*" and the section "IC BGA Soldering and Repair" in chapter five of this book.

Caution: It is the technician's responsibility to verify that the new parts being swapped with the old part in the device is in good condition before further investigation on the motherboard. Unlike other components that can be tested with the multi-meter, the LCD cannot be tested in like manner. The alternative is to test them on another similar device or try as many new replacement LCDs or flex connectors as are available. This is usually a dicey situation especially for permanently soldered flex connectors or fused LCD and flex units. Smartphones and tablets are connected with manually lift-able jacks with clips which is easier. The only challenge is during disassembly and separating the digitizer from the LCD. But for older models, whether it is a single unit purchased at a parts store or the technician has the parts in stock, multiple testing of LCDs or flex connectors without success results in loss of money if damaged in the process. In cases where the technician purchases one at a time from a phone parts store, the sellers hardly accept a return part (good/bad) once it has been soldered and you cannot blame them would you? Your soldering skills must be perfect or you might be the problem as well. But I trust you won't be the problem!

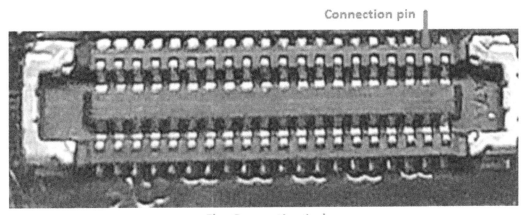

Flex Connection jack

Touchscreens

Touchscreens are available in different sizes. Their flexible (Flex) connectors usually have four (4) contact pins: [+], [-], [Rx], [Tx]. Rx is simply a data communication terminology for "Receive signal" while Tx is "Transmit signal". They are usually controlled by the CPU and operating system software. In some smartphones or tablets, an intermediate Interface IC or Touchscreen IC is present instead. Touchscreen problems manifest in the following ways;

- Whole or partial section of the screen not responding to touch input.
- One or more keys or icon not responding to touch.

Testing, Troubleshooting & Repair Procedure

To repair a touchscreen problem;

i.   Check the surface of the touchscreen for any scratch or physical damage.

ii. If the touchscreen is a resistive type touchscreen, go to the device settings and recalibrate the touchscreen. Resistive touchscreens are rare in the market now as the more responsive capacitive touchscreens are in vogue.

iii. Turn OFF and dismantle the mobile device to its component parts.

iv. Disconnect the touchscreen connector contact from the motherboard. Most of them have sensors which are detachable.

v.   Clean the contacts thoroughly with cleaning fluid and reconnect it back.

vi. Test the touchscreen to confirm whether the problem is solved.

vii. If the problem persists, replace with an alternative good touchscreen. This is the default and most feasible solution to touchscreen issues, except where the touchscreen itself is not the problem.

viii. Test again to check whether the problem is solved.

ix. If problem is yet unresolved, troubleshoot PCB tracks and motherboard control elements. Carry out reflow soldering on the touchscreen controller IC (sensor) or change the sensor. See section "IC BGA Soldering and Repair" in chapter five of this book.

x.   Consider reloading the mobile device software before or after step [ix] above if problem persists.

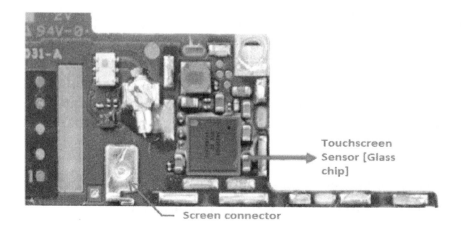

Touchscreen Sensor [Glass chip]

Screen connector

Keypad Faults

Smartphones and most tablets have moved away from traditional physical keypads to touchscreens. However, it is still possible to run into devices with keypads, so let's still talk about it.

Keypads are input user interface devices through which the mobile device receives command and control signal. They preceded the current prevalent virtual keyboard input system in touchscreen technologies. They consist of buttons arranged in a multi-grid array of rows and columns which bridges two separate physical electrical contacts when pressed down. The buttons are setup in a matrix arrangement. This allows a microcontroller IC to 'scan' the output pins to detect which of the buttons is being pressed.

The resulting analog electrical signal is fed into an ADC (Analogue-to-Digital Converter) connected to a BCD (Binary Coded Digits) decoder that is either separate or integrated into the CPU. The output is displayed on the LCD. When keypads fail, the following symptoms are observed;

- All or few specific buttons produce zero output on the display unit.
- Keystrokes causes the mobile device to restart or reboot.
- Response to keystrokes is very slow in producing an output or desired action.
- Keystrokes produces unexpected outcomes than is normal on the display unit.
- Response to keystrokes requires very hard pressure on the buttons.
- The back-light on the keyboard is not functioning or remains permanently ON.

The following are probable causes of malfunction of keypads;

a. Oxidation or corrosion of keypad contacts due to liquids.
b. Liquid on the motherboard (PCB).
c. Corrupted operating system software.
d. Virus activity.
e. Faulty control elements or ICs.
f. Damaged keypad buttons, part or whole unit.

Testing, Troubleshooting & Repair Procedure

Follow the steps below to troubleshoot and repair keypad faults;

i.   Whether it is a physical keypad or touchscreen, determine if the behavior is symptomatic of a software fault. If it is, flash the phone. But for hardware checks…

ii.   Turn OFF the mobile device and remove the battery, SIM and Memory card.

iii.   Dismantle the mobile device using the recommended tools described earlier.

iv.   Test the keypads in a partially disassembled state. This is because when in its assembled form, if there is a permanently pressed down side switch (side volume control buttons, camera etc.), it will affect the keypad functionality.

v.   If the keypads are not functioning, locate the keypad assembly on the front fascia of the mobile device and detach it from the motherboard. There are usually two or three layers consisting of plastic button (pad or carbon) a thin cellophane material laced with gum and concave cylindrical contacts array (*the concave form is such that it makes contact with the PCB's outer gold ring pad when at rest, on its outer edges. The upward curve at the center makes for non-contact with the inner gold ring pads except when pressed down, then it closes the circuit by bridging the two rings*) that is stuck to the PCB. Carefully peel off this cellophane. Do not tear or apply cleaning fluid on the gum. It will neutralize its sticky property making it unable to be fixed back in position after repair.

Figure 7.3a: Keypad PCB Contact

vi.   Clean the motherboard dual concentric circular gold contact pads (outer and inner circular pads separated by a ring). The outer ring for Rows while the inner ring is for Columns. See figure 6.2f above;

vii.   Using a sharp blade, scratch out oxidation coatings or dirt on the concave circular shiny metal contacts stuck on the reverse side of the cellophane material. Be careful to retain their positions on the material. Align and stick the cellophane back to the PCB contact pads.

viii.   Partially assemble the device, enough to power it ON and test the keypads one after the other.

ix.   Problem solved? End. If not, conduct a test by either directly pressing the keys on the flat cellophane covered contacts or using the outermost button overlay on the cellophane. If the problem is from the outermost buttons, change them. Else …

Figure 7.3b: Detachable Keypad PCB covered with cellophane

x.   Conduct a test by directly bridging the motherboard contact pads with a screwdriver or pressing the cellophane's concave circular metal discs on the PCB contact pads. If the fault is with the discs, you can change the whole material or change the circular discs one after the other.

xi.   If the problem persists, change the keypad assembly for cases where it is a detachable unit with a flex connector. Where it is not a separate unit from the PCB, test for continuity between rows and columns. If there is any break in electrical continuity, reconnect the PCB track. If ok, then keypad matrix is ok.

xii.   Trace the electrical connection and condition of the keypad control electronic components. Re-flow with rework soldering station's blower or use soldering iron to re-solder each component's contacts one after the other. If they are ok, test the keypad again after heat re-flow.

xiii.   If problem still persists, the next step is to re-flow the keypad IC (Microcontroller) and apply the knowledge gained in *Chapter 6: Electronics Fundamentals* of the first edition book "*Mobile Phones and Tablets Repairs: A Complete Guide for Beginners and Professionals*" and the section "IC BGA Soldering and Repair" in chapter five of this book.

Switches' Faults

When switches fail in mobile devices, it is evidenced by an obvious non-responsiveness to a desired function. For instance;

- When the power switch is pressed, the device should power ON/OFF, else it has failed.
- When the side volume key is pressed, it should either increase or decrease volume, else it has failed.
- When the camera button or switch is pressed, it should activate camera functionality, else it has failed.

Testing, Troubleshooting and Repair Procedure

Any failure to bring about the above listed responses might not always mean that the switch is the problem. Other such related faults have been discussed in other sections.

If however the fault at hand is determined to be with the switch, take the following actions;

i. Turn OFF the device and remove the battery, SIM and Memory Card.
xiv. Locate the relevant unresponsive switch and determine what type of switch you are dealing with based on the knowledge shared earlier about switch types in *Chapter 3: Basic Electronics and Circuits Analysis* of this book.
ii. If the switch is observed to be physically damaged, change immediately.
iii. If there is no observable physical damage, test with multi-meter to confirm if the switch is functional or not (See *'How to Test Various Components –Switches'* in Chapter six of this book).
iv. If it is functional, res-older its contacts on the PCB and test. If it is damaged and therefore non-functional, replace with a new one.

SIM and Memory Card Faults

SIM cards are the storage units in which telecommunication companies store the communication codes and subscriber information necessary for maintaining access to the mobile network.

Depending on the device to be repaired, SIMs come in full size, Micro-SIM size or NANO-SIM size.

SIM   Micro-SIM   Nano-SIM

Memory cards on the other hand are secondary extended memory chips used to provide extended storage capability to the mobile device, for storing user data.

There are a few faults associated with these two devices which we shall discuss shortly. The different ways these units fail are as discussed below;

SIM Card Faults

a. The notification, 'No SIM card' or 'Insert SIM card' is displayed on the device's screen (just like it normally does when no SIM is inserted), even though a SIM is inserted properly.
b. A SIM card is properly inserted but the device is not recognizing the presence of a Network.
c. 'Invalid SIM card' is displayed on the screen when SIM is inserted.

Testing, Troubleshooting and Repair Procedure

i.   Turn OFF the device and remove the battery.
ii. Based on the information displayed on the screen when SIM is inserted, take the following actions.
iii. For (a) above, confirm with another good SIM card if the mobile device would display the same message. If not, the problem is with the first SIM card. CHANGE SIM. If the same message is displayed (meaning that the device does not recognize SIM), the problem is with the device.
iv. Next, dismantle the mobile device.
v.   Check the SIM tray. The SIM tray has six contact pins that interface with the SIM card's copper surface which is subdivided into six.

Ensure that each pin from the PCB SIM tray has connectivity with the PCB contact pads.

vi. If any pin is broken, change the unit. If the pins have lost connectivity, re-solder and test.

vii. If SIM tray unit is OK, first do a thorough cleaning of the PCB with focus on the electronic components around the SIM tray area. Reflow surrounding electronic components with hot air. Test the SIM again.

viii. If problem persists, locate the SIM microcontroller chip (IC)-usually made of a very small glass in square shape. Apply hot air re-flow process to the chip (usually a small glass chip) with moderate hot air stream. Apply good soldering skills learnt in an earlier chapter. Test again.

ix. If problem persists, change microcontroller chip.

These steps above apply to all error messages in which the technician has determined that the SIM card itself is not the faulty device. If all else fails, do a flash programming of the mobile device.

Memory Card (MMC) Faults

When a phone is not recognizing the MMC, it is most often a hardware failure. However, sometimes the insertion of a memory card results in the mobile device restarting or rebooting. In such cases, the problem might be software related.

Testing, Troubleshooting and Repair Procedure

Check whether the memory card is working or not in another device. If not, replace it. If yes, then proceed as follows;

i. Turn OFF the mobile device, remove the SIM, MMC and disassemble.

ii. Turn straight any bent pins (if there are bent pins) of the Memory card slot/tray.

iii. Also clean the MMC socket with cleaning fluid and re-solder its contact terminals. Test whether the issue was resolved. If it is fine, end of repairs.

iv. If not ok, re-flow (BGA heating procedure) the MMC IC or change it.

v.   If problem persists, carry out a re-flow of the microprocessor. (Reason: All the connections of the MMC terminate at the micro-processor).

Network Faults

In earlier chapters, we learnt that a mobile phone is basically a radio, although digital mobile phones use the same radio technology in a different way. For instance, digital phones change analog voice signal into binary information (1 and 0) and then compress it, allowing multiple (up to ten) digital phones to occupy the same frequency spectrum equivalent to that occupied by one analog cell phone.

Communication takes place over a network. The basic functionality of a mobile device therefore, is to communicate over wireless network media. Any mobile device that fails to gain access to the network or communicate effectively over the network media has essentially become a brick.

Inside the mobile phone, there are lots of components and ICs which their failure will result in network connectivity problems. However, just like other fault correction processes, troubleshooting and fixing network related faults in mobile phones follow a systematic process.

Some common causes of network faults are;

- Antenna pads corroded, dirty or antenna unit not making proper contact with the antenna contact pads.
- Antenna, antenna cable or contacts is broken.
- Antenna switch not performing its functions hence damaged.
- Damaged power amplifier.
- RF chips or filters (Rx/Tx Saw Filters) may be damaged.
- RF signal generator (VCO) not functioning.
- RF processor (Analog baseband) not functional.
- Corrupt or invalid IMEI or software damage.

Mobile devices with Network access faults exhibit the following observable traits;

- "No Network" or "No Access" displayed on the screen (*Antenna/Antenna switch wire tracks broken, dirty contact pads, or dry broken soldered joints*).

- Carrier Network ID displayed on the screen without a single network signal icon bar. (*Software fault, require flash programming*).
- No outgoing calls but receives calls only (*Power Amplifier faulty*).
- User not reachable (No Call Reception) but can make calls (*Check Antenna Switch/ RF processor*).
- Signal bars show full on power on and disappear especially when trying to make or receive call (*check Power Amplifier [PA] especially (+ve) power supply line to it. Also track between Tx signal from PA to Antenna switch or change PA*).

Smartphones and Tablets' Antennas

There are multiple antennas in smartphones and tablets which supports the various cellular & non-cellular technologies in their design. The essence is to support the high data throughputs of the current 4G/LTE standard of mobile communication. The number of antennas depends also on the type of features implemented in the design of each model. Below is a list of the different antennas and what they support. They include;

- GSM 2G/3G/EVDO Multiple antennas for MIMO and diversity (for cellular service)
- GPS antenna
- Wi-Fi antenna (supporting latest standards like WLAN 802.11n & 802.11ac)
- NFC antenna (if the phone has Near Field Communication feature)
- Bluetooth antenna
- Wireless charging antenna

In LTE, multiple diversity paths are required for transmit and receive signals. However, phones cannot handle two frequencies on a single carrier SIM. Therefore, MIMO technology is combined with what is regarded as Carrier Aggregation (CA), whereby two or more frequencies are integrated into one envelop frequency, to double or triple data rates.

MIMO technology (2×2) is mostly used for better signal reception and larger data rates from the mobile network towers although the network providers usually deploy much more advanced MIMO (3×3 or higher) technology infrastructures. In summary, multiple cellular antennas are deployed in MIMO mode for LTE smartphones and tablets, although they serve the purpose of diversity in non-LTE operational modes like when using the phone in HSPA+ or 3G cellular.

Earlier basic and feature phones had just one multi-band antenna transmitting and receiving signals across multiple (two to five) frequency bands. Take a second look at this image below.

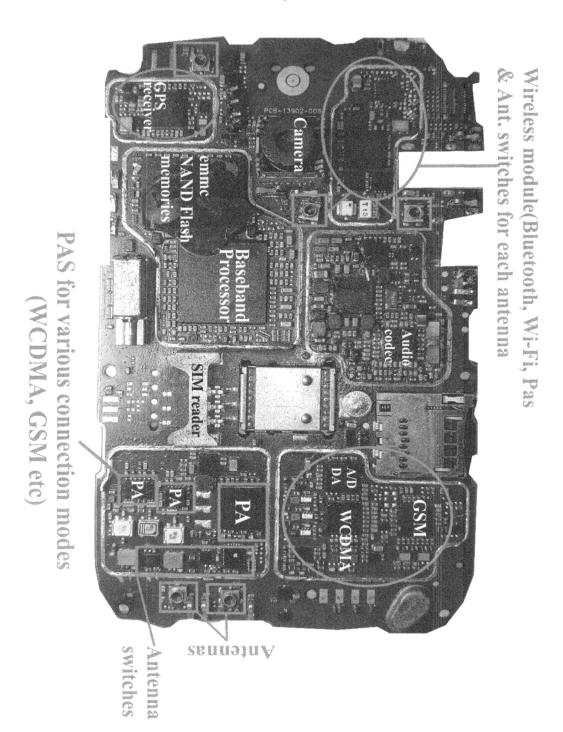

Testing, Troubleshooting and Repair Procedure

To repair network issues take the following steps;

i. Go to the mobile device's settings>Network settings>…and ensure the multi-band selection option is ON. For smartphones, there are options for 3G (WCDMA or HSPA) or both and 4G/LTE etc. This is to ensure that temporary network communication parameters available in the user's environment relative to the selected band or mode did not cause the network failure.

ii. If all network settings are correct, next is to power cycle the mobile device by switching it OFF for 15 minutes before switching it ON again. Observe the booting and network initialization routine. If the network service is restored, problem solved; If not then next step.

iii. Check the phone's IMEI by dialing the code - *#06#. The 15 digit IMEI number should appear on the screen and it should correspond to that written on the back label of the phone or in the settings of the phone. For double SIM phones, two number sets will appear for each SIM card slot. If the IMEI is bad, it will show a wrong number, write "invalid" or show question marks "????". The solution is to use an appropriate software tool to re-write or repair the IMEI. If the IMEI is ok, next…

iv. Power OFF the device, remove the battery and disassemble the unit for PCB access.

v. Using soft brush and a chemical solvent (IPA recommended) clean the entire PCB assembly; focus on the antenna pads and dry. Test to confirm whether the problem is resolved before taking the next step.

vi. If the problem persists, check whether the antenna is properly connected with its pins to the antenna contact pads (improvisation is allowed by making jumpers where necessary between antenna and antenna pads) and re-solder the antenna contacts and surrounding discrete electronic components. Test after re-soldering process. Smartphones use flexible long-running thin coaxial cables.

vii. If the problem persists, Trace the track between the antenna and the antenna switch (Tx/Rx Switch) and ensure connectivity if broken. This is because network search, network identification and authentication are carried out by the baseband processor in sync with the antenna switch/antenna pair. Test before next step.

viii. If the problem persists, although RF filters rarely get damaged, reflow-solder these components.

ix. If the problem persists, re-solder the antenna switch contacts. If it is still not ok, remove the antenna switch and make jumper between its Tx, Rx lines and antenna pads. Test before next step.

x. If the problem persists, the main component in the RF section is the RF processor. In some phones it is a BGA chip while some others in the older models, they are SMT Chips with visible side pins. Carry out re-flow soldering with care. Damaged RF processor leads to dead phone in many phones.

xi. The phone connects to the network using its software encoded with network control protocols which controls RF hardware components and also performs certain frequency tuning in collaboration with the CPU. This means that some network faults are as a result of a corrupted software. If all hardware repair procedures fail, a software flash programming is necessary as a last resort.

Camera Failure Faults

Cameras are integrated into mobile devices to provide users with the added capability to take snapshots and process still and motion pictures. They also fail just like other functional units in the mobile device. Some symptomatic behaviors when they fail are;

- The device displays a message "Camera module not ready"
- The display becomes dark with no images in view when camera is activated
- No response when camera is activated

Testing, Troubleshooting and Repair Procedure

After checking the mobile device's settings to confirm that all settings are in order, take the following steps;

i. Turn OFF the device, remove SIM, MMC and disassemble the device.

ii.   Use brush to clean the camera connectors with IPA or any other solvent and test. If ok, End.

iii.   If the problem is not solved replace Camera.

iv.   If the problem persists, replace the Camera module (PCB connecting jack).

v.   If all hardware repair procedures fail, a software flash programming is necessary as a last resort.

Restarting/Rebooting Mobile Device Faults

Devices like mobile phones, tablets, or PDAs may experience automatic intermittent power cycling issues when an abnormal condition exists in their circuitry. A mobile device has a power cycling fault if;

- It reboots continuously.
- It reboots during a phone call (transmit or receive).
- It reboots when the keypads are being used or when a particular action is being taken by the user just after functioning normally over a period of time.
- It gets excessively hot intermittently (overheating) and then reboots.

Take the following actions to repair:

i.   Remove the battery and disassemble the device if it doesn't respond to the power switch to turn OFF.

ii.   Remove all peripheral units attached to the PCB.

iii.   Service the PCB using brush and cleaning fluid. Using hot air, carry out reflow procedure on the whole PCB components. Test.

iv.   If the problem persists, with the device dismantled, connect the PCB to power supply (battery or D.C power supply). Attach peripheral units one after the other because any one of them could be the cause.

v.   Switch ON the device and allow it to be ON for at least 2 minutes.

vi.   Lay your thumb on the various ICs and other components on the PCB. Feel, to determine which component is getting excessively hot.

vii.   If there is any such component, remove and replace that component or IC. For ICs, carry out reflow soldering procedure. If problem is not solved, remove the IC and re-ball (BGA soldering procedure).

viii.   If there was no overheating component or IC, reassemble the device and carry out Flash programming or boot sector formatting with the appropriate software tool.

ix.   If step (viii) fails, the Microprocessor is the faulty component. Dismantle the device again and carry out reflow/BGA soldering repair procedure on the Microprocessor. After any such repair on processors, flashing the phone is a must.

x.   But if the rebooting occurs during phone calls, both the PA (Power Amplifier) and CPU (Microprocessor) are possible suspects, especially the PA.

PCB or Motherboard Faults

The Printed Circuit Board PCB, Mainboard or Motherboard of a mobile device provides surface mount space and wiring circuitry for every electronic component or device that make up the mobile phone. PCBs develop faults and as well damage beyond repair. In Chapter 6 (Electronics Fundamentals) of the first edition book *"Mobile Phones and Tablets Repairs: A Complete Guide for Beginners and Professionals"*, in-depth details about the motherboard was fully explored.

Like I said earlier, knowledge and understanding about the device a technician is fixing and the functionality of its component parts makes for a better technician. It enhances your technical judgments and speeds up your capacity to deliver in good time, as well as to earn good money.

PCB faults occur in one or more of the following ways;

a.   Short-circuit in the internal wiring
b.   Open-circuit in the internal wiring
c.   Damaged contact pads for surface mount components

The above three common ways a PCB can fail could all be traceable to water or any other salty or mineral liquid.

Water Damage Faults

Water is not good for electronics especially where there is a tight enclosure as is the case with smartphones and tablet phones. Once water is trapped underneath the ICs or the surface of the PCB, it causes corrosion.

Corrosion occurs as a result of oxidation of the metal contacts which creates rust, corroding the metallic contacts of the surface mounted components. As corrosion spreads, the resistance between circuit components drops. On the surface, the rust creates bridges between adjacent components that by design should not be connected together. These 'bridges' are short-circuits. Pits and cracks also occur in places where current freely flowed before the liquid damage. This results in what is called electrical 'open-circuits'. The affected components might fail permanently or temporarily pending the removal of the 'short-circuit' or reconnection of the 'open-circuit'. Also, corrosion can eat up the fibrous coating of the PCB in an irreparable manner.

Testing, Troubleshooting and Repair Procedure

Cleaning the Motherboard

Electronic boards are usually cleaned using various chemical solvents. The recommended chemical for mobile phone PCBs is Isopropyl Alcohol (IPA) also called Isopropanol. It is an effective cleaning agent that dries as quickly as it is applied leaving no harmful residue on the motherboard like acidic oils. It dissolves oils, alkaloids, gums, natural resins etc. and removes thermal pastes from IC packages. Because of their relative high cost, most technicians resort to using readily available fluids like Methylated spirits.

Methylated spirits are actually ethanol mixed with Methanol and some poisonous additives. In some cases they are dyed to change their color. They also contain a little quantity of Isopropyl alcohol and other chemical additives. The disadvantage of using methylated spirit is that it leaves residue of toxic oils on the PCB after use. When used, a technician must carefully dry out (burn out) the oily molecules with continual streams of hot air especially underneath the ICs.

There are many cases where use of IPA to clean a water damaged phone would instantly restore the phone to normal working conditions whereas on alternatively using Methylated spirit, the PCB refuses to power ON until after painstaking drying routines are applied.

If what is being used is an ultrasonic cleaner, immerse the PCB in a soap solution and wash thoroughly with brush before putting it into the machine. Before that, delicate peripheral units like camera, LCD, microphone, speaker, and ringer etc. must be detached from the PCB and kept aside safely. Regardless of whatever cleaning method is adopted, recognize that the objective is to keep a PCB as dirt-free, water-free, oil-free, and alkaloids-free as its pre-fault condition.

Like I wrote earlier about the mentality a technician must adopt towards every repair process, the foremost objective should be to return a faulty

Smartphone or Tablet back to that state or condition in which the manufacturer made and introduced it into the market. If it was initially functioning, your mental state should be such as to eliminate with every process possible, any foreign causative agent introduced into the device that may be preventing it from normal operation. That way, solving problems will be a lot easier.

PCB Short- Circuit

When short-circuit conditions exist in a phone's PCB, the phone will shut down completely. This is what is commonly regarded as a 'dead phone' condition because it arrived at the technician's service center, dead – non-responsive, whether temporarily or permanently.

Short circuits are conditions in an electrical circuit where two distinct parallel electric wires or conductors of positive (+) and negative (-) polarity, have their paths crossed at any point in the circuit. In PCBs however, wires are replaced with printed copper tracks.

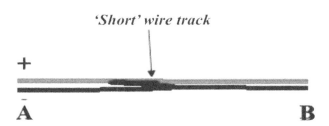

Short circuits on PCBs can create any of the following faulty behavior in a mobile device;

    a. Power-On failure
    b. Overheating of the mobile device
    c. Fast battery drain
    d. Mobile device frequently freeze or hang
    e. Restarting/Rebooting of mobile device.

Testing, Troubleshooting and Repair Procedure

To test if a motherboard or PCB is short-circuited;

i.   Turn OFF (if it is still working albeit abnormally) the mobile phone or device and disassemble it.

ii.   Using your multi-meter for continuity testing, locate the battery terminals of the device. There are usually different types of battery contacts: 2-terminals type, 3-terminals type and the 4-terminals type. Whichever type the device came with, the first and the last pin counting from left to right are the positive (+) and negative (-) contacts respectively. The battery-side contacts have the mark (+) and (-) on the battery so you can use that as a guide too.

iii. With the positive (+) probe of the multi-meter, touch the negative (-) battery contact terminal on the PCB while the negative (-) probe is on the positive (+) of the battery terminals.

iv.   If there is continuity (if using the buzzer test point and it beeps or using normal resistance measurement, it reads 0Ω), the PCB is 'shorted' (short-circuited).

v.   If using a D.C supply machine, select a supply voltage equivalent to the mobile device's battery output voltage. Connect the probes: (+) probe to (+) battery connector terminal; (-) probe to (-) battery connector terminal. If there is a short circuit in the PCB, the Ammeter will output a current value in Amperes (A). If not, it will give a zero output.

vi.   Clean the whole circuit-board with IPA making sure underneath all the ICs is thoroughly washed. Repeat the flow of fluid underneath the chips several times. You might need to soak the PCB for about 120 to 180 minutes in a recommended solvent before drying and then reflow soldering is applied.

vii. Test to see if short circuit still exists.

viii. Investigate the source of short circuit and eliminate it. This is how;

ix.   Remove all peripheral components from the PCB and test again for a 'short'.

x.   If the short circuit is no more, begin adding the components one after the other to determine the causative agent. One of the components must be the culprit. Keep connecting them to the PCB one after the other until the fault-triggering component is exposed.

xi.   However, if the short circuit persists, continue the investigation on the PCB.

xii.   For peripheral components, determine whether it is the component that needs replacement or a lack of supply at its terminals. Also, apply component testing skills learnt in this book, to the discrete electronic components. A track can be good but the electronics (like burnt capacitors, resistors etc.) surrounding a peripheral component may have failed, making it not to function. If that happens, remove the component, check if the 'short' is no more existent and replace with an exact, similar part on the same spot.

xiii.   Test once again for any presence of a short circuit.

xiv.   Connect the PCB to its battery, press the power switch to ON and keep it in this position for 10-20 seconds, whether the board powers ON or not. Remove the battery and immediately check if any component or IC is heating. Any component which is heating up is most likely shorted. Remove it and check again. If the problem is eliminated, replace the overheating IC or component.

xv.   If short circuit still exists, download PCB wiring diagram from the internet or use Easy Draw software for phones.

xvi.   Begin a wiring track trace using the circuit diagram as a guide and a digital multi-meter for continuity testing. Any two contacts which are by design not meant to intersect but are showing interconnection would be the fault line.

xvii.   If all efforts so far failed, then the PCB has gone beyond repair.

PCB Open-Circuit

Broken PCB wiring tracks are referred to as open-circuits. Open circuits might occur due to a broken positive (+) or negative (-) polarity electrical track, preventing the circuit from completing by stopping the flow of current. Due to the design of motherboards with multiple layers of board fused together, breaks can occur either internally or on the surface of the PCB.

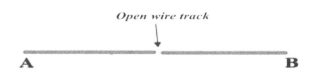

Testing, Troubleshooting and Repair Procedure

In order to fix broken tracks in the PCB circuitry, a circuit tracing process needs to be carried out. 'Track-tracing' is used to check for broken tracks on the Printed Circuit Boards (PCB).

These tracks are voltage, current and data supply lines to every component connected to the circuit board. Any component starved of this supply cannot function. A PCB can only be 'dead' if the open circuit occurs on its power supply line between battery and the power supply system.

Therefore, take the following steps to solve broken track problems;

i.   Track tracing is a continuity measurement process. Get your multi-meter ready on the continuity test buzzer mode selector.

ii.   Determine what type of failure is being investigated ranging between power failure and component failures.

iii.   Download the device's PCB wiring diagram. This is most times available if you search on the internet.

iv.   Get your jumper wire roll, magnifier or microscope and soldering equipment handy.

v.   Begin the trace, testing the various component interconnections, terminal to terminal according to the wiring diagram

vi.   For peripheral components, determine if it is the component that needs replacement or a lack of supply current at its terminals. Also, apply component testing skills learnt in this book to the electronic components.

vii.   A track can be good but the electronics (like burnt capacitors, resistors etc.) surrounding a peripheral component may have failed (open-circuited), making it not to function. If that happens, remove the component; if its open-circuit condition is as a result of a break, reconnect with a piece of cable. If not, replace similar part on that spot.

viii. If a PCB wiring diagram is not available online, Google library of cached images provide an alternative. Other professionals in the mobile phone repair community worldwide share jumper track trace solutions that have worked. Use your sound judgment to verify and apply same.

ix.   Where a track is broken, use an insulated jumper wire to make relevant cable link.

Improvisation

When there is adequate knowledge of the theoretical and practical design of a system as this book is trying to equip the reader, intelligent and creative improvisation would become handy and commonplace to the technician.

Technical improvisation refers to the ability of a technician to devise workable equivalent solutions relative to standard practice which were not planned before-hand, but applied on the job for a particular instance.

What this means is that a situation may warrant your devising a solution based on a mix of technical experience working on several other devices. For instance, there are components that are meant for a particular device or model but which can be modified to fit into a customized solution for another model successfully. There are components which may not be available for a repair job for which your application of creative solutions will be needed. Whatever you do, ensure that such solutions are durable.

Some Frequently Asked Questions

Hardware and Software Related Questions

Q1. *What is Flashing and formatting of a phone?*

Answer: Flashing a phone is a process whereby the firmware/operating system of the phone is erased and reloaded. However, when you format a phone the arrangement of data in the phone which must have been altered or rearranged in the memory areas either by usage or virus infection is reordered and realigned with the file system to comply with the phone's default/normal programming within the Operating System. After formatting a phone, it returns to its default state; all user data are deleted and bugs or viruses are removed.

Q2. *What are the different types of flash memory in a phone?*

a. NOR flash and b. NAND flash

Q3. *What are the various types of CPU brands in China phones?*

There are different CPUs and flash types;

    A. MTK (MediaTek)
    B. SPD (Spreadtrum)
    C. TI (Texas Instrument)
    D. MSTAR CPU
    E. RDA/ Coolsand CPU
    F. Infineon
    G. Broadcom

Q4. *What is the difference between NAND and NOR Flash?*

(i) NOR Flash: Intel® introduced the first commercial NOR-type flash chip in 1988. NOR-based flash has long erase and write times, but provides full address and data buses, allowing random access to any memory location.

(ii) NAND Flash: NAND is the second type of flash chip. It has faster erase and write times, and requires a smaller chip area per cell. NAND-flash has about ten times the endurance of NOR flash chip. However, the I/O (Input/Output) interface of NAND-flash does not provide a random-access external address bus. Rather, data must be read on a page block basis, with typical block sizes of hundreds to thousands of bits.

Q5. *What are the labels of the different data test-points of phones?*

Answer: Pin-outs data test points for software flash access are:

RX
TX
GND
D+
D-
VPP

Q6. *What is a jumper?*

Answer: A short length of wire used temporarily to complete a circuit or to bypass a break in a circuit.

Q7. *When a previously working phone that has a good screen but a software fault before it was flashed, displays white (blank illuminated) screen after Flash, what could be the cause?*

Answer: Use of wrong (or lower) flash file version might cause it. Download the correct file, especially the highest available version and flash again.

Q8. *When one inserts a charger and the phone says "Bad contact charger" or any other error notification, what could be the reason and solution.*

Answer: This could be due to excess current being drawn from the charger. Every phone needs a required voltage/current in order to charge. Try replacing the charger as a first step before trying out the solution recorded in this book.

Q9. *When a phone 'hangs or freezes" after power on, is it a software or hardware fault?*

ANSWER: It can either be a hardware fault or a software fault, but try the following.

i. Remove the side volume key buttons.
ii. Check the keypad for any likely stuck-in keys. Release if any.
iii. Disassemble the phone and clean it with a solvent.
iv. Reflow solder the microprocessor,
v. Finally try software flash.

Q10. *When a phone restarts during initialization, begins and gets stuck in endless unsuccessful network search, what could be done?*

Answer:
i. If the device is a China phone, Format or carry out a full flash with any China phone software flasher. If it does not solve the problem, remove or replace the Bluetooth controller IC (tested in majority of China phones).
ii. If the phone is not a China phone, reflow the microprocessor or flash the phone.

Q11. *When a phone boots to a white, blank display what should be done?*

Answer: First of all check if you could receive or make call.

i. If yes then it would be a hardware related fault, Change the LCD
ii. If not, then resolve it as a software problem

Q12. *What does a flash file contain?*

Answer: Flash files contain Firmware in legacy phones and Firmware + Operating System in Smartphones. Operating system software could be iOS (iPhones) or Android OS, the two major mobile operating systems. Windows Mobile OS by Microsoft is already discontinued.

Q13. *When a phone shows "Contact Service" what does it mean and what should be done?*

Answer: The message displayed shows that one or more parts of the software are not able to execute properly, triggering the watchdog processor which is able to detect that an error has occurred. This happened in the older generation of phones, specifically, NOKIA. So, when a phone is powered ON, it executes a self-test routine; if one or more components fail, the message "contact service" is displayed on the screen. Therefore to fix this problem;

i.   The first action is to flash the phone. If it continues to show the message;

ii.   Disassemble the phone.

iii.   Using soft brush and a cleaning solvent like IPA, 'service' the phone's PCB by washing and drying with hot air station.

iv.   Ensure the solvent gets underneath the ICs and then carry out hot air- reflow across the PCB.

v.   Couple the phone back and power ON.

vi.   If not solved, carry out complete hardware troubleshooting and BGA reflow on the Power IC.

Finally, as a general advice again, Google-search of a phone model's name for instance with 'dead phone solution' appended will direct you to numerous video solution tips other professionals applied for a specific fault which was successful.

If you click 'images' after the search result, you might find helpful soldering, PCB wiring diagrams, and wiring track jumper cable-section images discovered by other professionals as a shortcut to digging into circuit diagrams by yourself. Most people can use Google too, but the difference is in understanding what is shown, how to disassemble, how to solder and many other knowledge and experience gained in this book and from daily work and familiarity with phones.

PART 2

SOFTWARE REPAIR TECHNIQUES

Chapter 8

Software Repairs

Smartphones and tablets are *computerized* electronic devices built with hardware and software components. This is the simplest descriptive summary of the design of smartphones and tablets, in the context of repairs and maintenance.

In the first two parts of this book, focus had been on familiarizing and dealing with the hardware components, hardware tools, and hardware repair procedures required for fixing faults in a smartphone or tablet. In this part three module, our focus would be on software related faults associated with smartphones or tablets and the software tools needed.

Software faults in phones require software solutions. Faults which manifest as a malfunction in certain hardware components are as a result of a failure or corruption of the software codes coordinating the operation of such hardware.

Phone repair software tools are programming tools designed with the capability to read and write software program files from and into the flash memory of a phones for the purpose of upgrade, repair or change of corrupted software in the mobile device. Phone software repair tools are therefore different from the Phone software itself. Each phone software, usually called "flash file" comprises of the written programs specific only to its model as designed by the manufacturer.

Generally, "Software" refers to any code of routines, instructions, commands or protocols that define and guide the operation of hardware, (including granting access to user input commands) in such a way as to control a system unit to perform specific operations. Once a programmer defines a structured set of instructions for the sole purpose of influencing computer hardware to perform specific functions, it is called software.

Phone or Computer software consists of programs, libraries and related non-executable data such as data stored in the phone like music, personal notes and documents, contacts, files etc. Software is non-tangible (unlike hardware it cannot be seen or touched).

A Computer or phone's hardware and software needs each other and neither can actually function without the other.

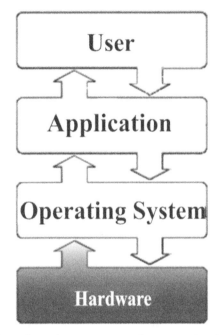

Information flow chart in a computer between Application software,
Operating system software and the User input
Source: https://en.wikipedia.org/software

Figure 8.1

Understanding Mobile Smartphone Software

Software in a phone or computer can be divided into the following categories:

Application software

These are software that uses the computer system or mobile device to perform special functions or entertainment beyond the basic operation of that computer device. They extend the device's utilization capacity. There are many different types of application software for smartphones and tablets in the iOS and Android App stores. An example of this is any application downloaded from Google play store or iTunes store.

System software

System software is any software that runs, operates or influences the computer hardware directly in order to provide basic functionality needed by users and other applications. One example of System software is the Operating system software.

Operating System software

They are essential collections of software that manages resources and provides common services for other software (e.g. Application software) that runs "on top" of them. Supervisory programs, boot loaders, shells and window systems are core parts of operating systems. In practice, an operating system comes bundled with additional software (including some application software) so that a user can potentially do some work with a computer that only has an operating system fresh out of production. For instance, when a new smartphone or tablet boots up, besides the basic Call app, SMS app and a few others, third party company apps like Facebook, Twitter and Instagram are preloaded. Where they are not part of the original OS flash file, the user has to manually download the apps from the App store. The same goes for a new computer system and the Windows or Macintosh macOS operating systems.

Device drivers

These types of software controls specific devices, externally attached to a computer. Each connecting device needs at least one corresponding device driver. They can be likened to interpreters that interpret the communication protocols between the device and the computer system it connects to; required for both interface and operational efficiency within the computer system.

Utilities

Utility software is a computer program designed to assist users in the maintenance and care of their computing devices.

Malicious software or malware

These are software developed to harm and disrupt computing devices. Examples of such malicious software are viruses, malwares, Trojan horses and any such software code which its intention is to harm the user or the device.

Smartphone Operating Systems (MobileOS)

A mobile operating system is simply the main system software platform on which all other programs run, on mobile devices. They are specifically designed to run on mobile devices such as mobile phones, smartphones, PDAs, tablet computers and other handheld devices. This is similar to the same way the Windows Operating Systems, Macintosh or Linux Operating Systems controls respective laptop or desktop computers.

The operating system determines the functions and features available on any mobile device, including the types of third-party applications a mobile device can run as well as the hardware functionalities. Below are some predominantly popular mobile OS today and relegated OS. They include;

1. Android OS by Google Inc.
2. iphone OS / iOS by Apple

Relegated Operating Systems;

3. Blackberry OS by Research In Motion (RIM)
4. Windows Mobile (Windows Phone 7) by Microsoft
5. Symbian OS by Nokia
6. MeeGo OS by Nokia & Intel
7. Palm OS
8. WebOS by Palm & HP
9. Bada by Samsung Electronics

Firmware

Firmware is used to refer to microcode software that runs in electronic and computing systems <u>held</u> specifically in non-volatile memory devices like ROM, EEPROM or flash memory. They are low level software codes that provide control, monitoring and data manipulation of engineered products at basic level, providing services to higher level software like the operating system. In embedded systems like mobile phones, firmware might be the only program running on the system, providing all functions in some phones (basic and feature phones) while in others like smartphones or tablets they are combined with an operating system. The flash files used for software repairs are actually firmware files. Flash memory allows firmware to be updated without physically removing an integrated circuit from the system.

For basic and feature phones that mostly had smaller storage capacity and far less application software processing, EEPROMs were mostly used.

NAND-flash storage with its larger memory capacity has enabled the use of larger operating system software that are feature rich, implementing a large bouquet of functions we enjoy today in smartphones and tablets..

Real Time Operating Systems (RTOS)

Every mobile device or smartphone in reality runs two operating systems instead of one. Apart from the mobile operating system that is very obvious to users and professionals like the Android OS, iOS or Windows and so on, it also runs a proprietary (manufacturer owned/specific) smaller operating system that manages everything related to radio. A real-time operating system is required for this purpose because radio functionality is highly timing-dependent.

This operating system is stored in EEPROM in some phones or NVRAM (remember Flash is a type of NVRAM) in others and runs on the baseband processor. Real time operating system running in a mobile device is very powerful. Compared to RTOS is the Computer BIOS (Basic Input Output System).

Requirements for the Flash Programming Procedure

The software program files for phones (OS or firmware) are usually downloaded and stored in a computer system. In order to transfer these files properly into a mobile device (smartphone, tablet, feature or basic phone) there has to be a communication link between the computer and the mobile phone, smartphone or tablet.

Computers have in-built communication ports, some of which includes the following;

- Serial ports

- Parallel ports

- USB (Universal Serial Bus) ports

- Ethernet ports

- VGA (Video Graphics Adapter) ports

- PS/2 ports

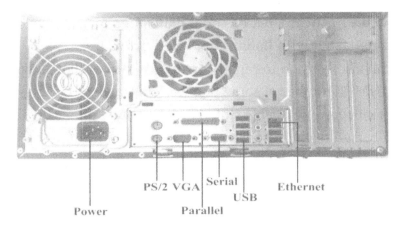

Figure 8.2: Computer ports

The USB technology has overtaken the older serial and parallel port systems although they still exist on the main boards of computers. Every product designed for interface in any way with a computer these days are fitted with USB ports. This includes mobile phones.

However, it is not all mobile phones whose software files (firmware or OS) can be transferred into its ROM or flash memory directly through a USB/serial/parallel cable connection to the computer. If it were mainly so, programmers who write software programs for phone repair will go hungry due to piracy and free internet downloads. Also, the repair software applications for most phone brands are not provided freely by their manufacturers. Third-party application developers with access to the mobile product's APIs (Application Programming Interface) leveraged that opportunity to create repair software applications referred to as flash software, with securely encrypted smart-card USB boxes.

Phone flasher boxes or simply "flashers" are mainly used for the following;

- To recover user data from dead or faulty mobile phones that otherwise will not provide access to data stored on their internal memory.
- To update or replace software that is stored in the mobile phone's Read Only Memory (ROM) or Non-Volatile Flash Memory (NVRAM). This software as we have learnt here is also commonly referred to as "firmware" and is usually pre-installed on phones by the manufacturer of the phone such as iPhone, Samsung, Sony-Ericsson, Huawei, and so on.
- To add language support and set regional settings for mobile phones. For instance, changing language settings can enable a user that bought

a phone with a firmware that has no Italian language support by default, to re-flash it with Italian supported firmware.

- Flashers can also be used to repair corrupted IMEI or illegally used to change the IMEI number of some phones. This in effect enables criminals to illegally re-enable stolen or lost mobile phones which may have been barred from the network by telecommunication carriers in some countries.

- They are used for unlocking SIM restrictions, User security locks, carrier based locks or call restrictions. SIM unlock is legal in some countries and illegal in others

- Finally they are used to replace corrupted firmware and operating system software with a good one as part of a fault correction procedure.

Features and Components of Flasher Software and Boxes

Phone flashers comprises of a combination of;

- The Software suite and Installation drivers.
- The hardware (USB flasher smart-card box).
- Service cables.
- Flash files for various supported mobile phone brands and models.

There are two main categories of Software flasher tools:

- Original (Branded) software tool boxes and
- Cloned or Cracked (Non-branded) tool boxes or software

Table 7.1: Features of Original and Cloned Flasher Tool boxes/ Software

Original (Branded) Tools	Cloned (Non-branded) Tools
They have well-known names and model numbers.	They have no known names and are much cheaper than branded boxes
They have unique serial numbers.	They combine the phone support of more than one branded flasher box.

Some boxes need activation. Software, updates and support is provided for these boxes. The level of support varies depending on the box manufacturer.	They support the addition of a smartcard from branded flasher boxes.
It is easier to get support for them in forums and on other support websites. Most major manufacturers have dedicated active threads on GSM Forum by ZFrank.	Do not usually come with any software and or drivers and places the responsibility on the buyer to find the software from other sources. No after sales support
They are widely used by professional repair service technicians.	Usage is rare among good repair professionals.
The boxes are usually sold with quality service cables.	Some come with a few service cables; others do not come with any.
They are sold by recognized retailers and an "Authorized reseller list" is often found on the manufacturer's website.	They are sold in the open market.
Their USB interface serve as a power source so they do not usually require an external power supply to function.	Some require the use of external power source not included in the purchase.

Flasher dongles

These are also used for mobile phone flashing but differ from the flasher boxes in their minimal functionality. Most dongles are used as extension cards to flasher boxes; can serve also for remote unlocking and de-branding of phones.

MX Key dongle

CS Tool Dongle

Credit: Ipmart.com
Figure 8.3: Sample Flasher Dongles

Flasher Cables and Interfaces

The flasher box typically connects to the mobile device through a special cable made for that phone model referred to as a "Service cable". One end of the cable is the standard RJ-45 Ethernet networking cable interface which connects to the RJ-45 port on the flasher box. The other end is a matching phone's USB/Data port connector or a set of data test point contact pins that make contact with the mobile phone's Joint Test Action Group (JTAG) or the Mbus/Fbus connections.

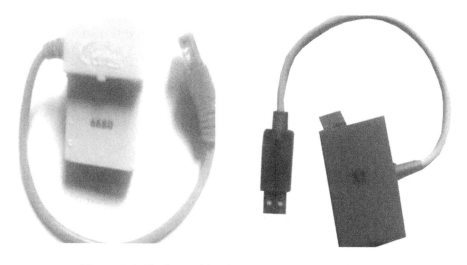

Figure 8.4: Flasher cables for Legacy Feature phones

Figure 8.5: Normal USB cables serve as Flasher cables for smartphones and tablets

Software Faults Diagnosis

The following symptoms lead to the diagnosis of a phone's behavior as a software fault;

- When a phone is frequently restarting automatically.
- When a phone is frequently switching off automatically without the power switch pressed or switch-OFF initiated by the user.
- When the phone switches OFF or reboots as soon as a particular folder like gallery, message inbox or other is opened.
- When some of the phone's applications which came with the OS refuse to function properly.
- Incomplete booting stuck at logo.
- When a phone does not switch-ON, especially without physical damage being a cause. This could be as a result of a corrupted OS.
- When a phone frequently freezes or hangs.
- When a phone processes its applications, user requests and commands very slowly.
- A phone starts up but is blank, inoperable and possibly with some indication light.
- A phone displays "Contact Service" or "Contact Retailer".

Installation Guide for Phone Software Tools

The appropriate software for each type of flasher box is usually made available through the official support site for the flasher box manufacturer. Each flasher box has a unique serial number which is usually displayed in the software suite's user interface dialog box after it has been properly installed. Also, when you purchase the flasher box from an accredited reseller or directly from the manufacturer, you are allotted a username and password for access to secure resources on their web servers.

It is required that the right driver for both the flasher box and various types of mobile devices are chosen. This information can be gotten from the flasher box manufacturer's support sites where they update the drivers frequently. Sometimes an older version of a USB driver and software bundle may run perfectly with some phone models while a newer USB driver and software bundle will not work with that same device.

Before using a flasher box, the following requirements must be in place in order to ensure a successful operation;

- USB drivers for the flasher box hardware in addition to the phone repair software should be installed in the computer **before** connecting the USB cable to the flasher box.
- If a specific version of the repair software does not work properly with a particular phone model or range of phone models, it is recommended that both the flasher box's repair software and its associated USB drivers be completely uninstalled from the computer system. Reboot the computer after uninstall completes and try another USB driver and software version until the appropriate driver and software match is found.
- Obtain information about the best version of driver for each type of device from phone repair forums or in the flasher box's support site. GSM forum by ZFrank remains a rich resource site for technicians as all the manufacturers maintain an active presence with threads of information on the site..
- A Flasher box's specific guidelines are usually available on the flasher box manufacturer's website. Read these guidelines for directions.
- Flash-files (firmware files) for each brand, model or type of mobile device supported by a particular flasher box are also available for download from the flasher box manufacturer's website. This is the

reason it is best to buy a branded flasher box. Some flash-files are flasher box-specific for given models of phones. Get the information from there as well. Flash-files are also available on many sites shared by other repair professionals. Be cautious about using any off-the-internet file.

- Finally be computer literate.

Minimum System Requirements for Software Flash Repair

The following are the required provisioning (provisioning involves the process of preparing and equipping a system to allow it to provide new services to its users) on any desktop or laptop computer any technician wishes to use for phone repairs' software flash programming. This section is meant to serve as a guide to the reader for organizing a computer system for the task of repairs.

Hardware Requirements

The following are minimum requirement which can be exceeded, depending on the available resources;

- 250 GB Hard Disk Drive - HDD (Minimum requirements) extensible internally or with external storage up to 2 Terabytes or more of hard disk storage
- 2GB RAM (Random Access Memory) minimum requirement
- 2.30 GHz Processor (minimum requirement)
- USB 2.0 ports

Software Requirements

Computer desktop or Laptop running Windows Operating System (32-bit or 64-bit Operating System is fine although you might encounter some useful applications that would require a 64-bit system. So why not have a 64-bit system). Windows XP (support has been retired by Microsoft)/ Windows Vista / Windows 7/ are all sufficient for most applications. Newer versions are beginning to support Windows 10 Operating system

WinRAR

WinRAR is Microsoft Windows® version of the RAR archiver - a powerful tool which allows one to create, manage and control archive files.

There are several versions of RAR, for a number of operating environments: Windows, Linux, FreeBSD, and Mac OS X.

There are two versions of RAR for Windows:

- Version with graphical user interface - WinRAR.exe;
- Command line console (text mode) version - Rar.exe.

WinRAR and WinRAR self-extracting modules require Windows XP or later versions. This application is important to the technician because most flash files and other useful files downloaded from the internet are in the archived format. Compressed archives combine multiple files into a single file to make them easier to transport or save on disk space. Zip is the most-widely used format, used by the Windows operating system. RAR is also a very popular and flexible format. Without the application installed in your computer, the archived useful content cannot be extracted.

One great benefit of having your files in .zip or.rar format is that viruses will not corrupt the files. It is a recommended practice to extract any needed file for flashing, use it, delete the file to conserve disk space (leaving the main file as a .rar or .zip file) and repeat the same process each time the file is needed to protect against virus.

Here is a screenshot that shows how these files look;

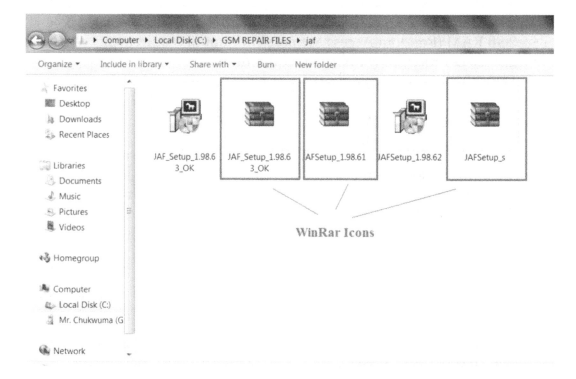

To extract the needed file, right click on it as below and select "Extract Here" or "Extract…" which will open the file path menu to direct the extraction to any desired location in the computer.

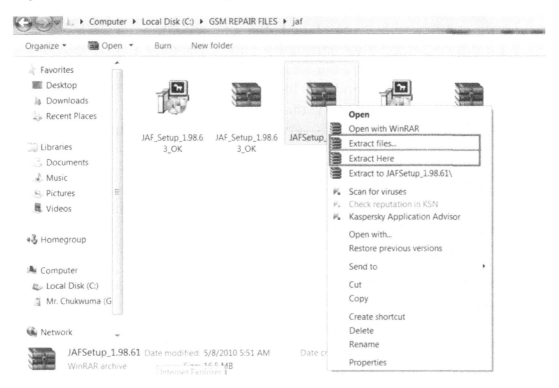

Software Repair Terminologies and Procedures

Every professional services sector have their lingua, terms and naming scheme necessary for communication among professionals. It is important when practicing in the field and makes for easy interaction and sharing of useful ideas.

In practice, access to materials, helpful guides and resources on the internet would only be possible and helpful when it is understood and interpreted correctly. Therefore, pay attention to the following terminologies often used and their meanings.

Flash Programming Terminologies

"Bricked" Phone

When a mobile device would not switch ON in any way, and therefore is in a non-functional state due to either a serious configuration error, corrupted firmware, or a hardware failure, it is regarded as 'Bricked".

A phone in a bricked state for all intents and purposes, is as useful as a literal brick. When a mobile phone is stuck in a boot loop for instance, it is not "fully" bricked; also a phone that boots straight into recovery mode is considered as a partially bricked phone.

Bricking usually results from a failed attempt to update a device. Most electronic devices, especially smartphones and tablets have an OTA (Over-The-Air) update procedure that must not be interrupted before completion. Should such an unwanted condition like power failure during the process happen, or any form of user intervention, or other reasons, the existing firmware might become partially overwritten and unusable. The risk of software corruption can therefore be minimized by taking all possible precautions against interruption during such processes.

"Bricking" can also be caused by installing the wrong firmware, firmware version, firmware with errors or for a different revision of the hardware and by viruses or other malicious software.

Bricking is classified into two types: *soft brick* and *hard brick*.

Soft bricked devices will boot unsuccessfully and get stuck on boot-up brand logo, or reboots continuously. Sometimes it shows a white blank screen (called White screen) when in use. Some of the major reasons for soft brick are;

- Software bugs.
- Viruses/malwares.
- Corrupt firmware installation.
- Attempted rooting failure.
- Flashing a custom recovery image to a device with a locked boot loader.
- Invalid memory caches.
- Wrong read/write permissions.

Flashing or system reset (hard or soft reset) that clears all the internal memory can recover a device from a soft brick state. For instance some phones usually show a single blinking red light while others like iOS devices show a completely black or white screen with only an Apple logo when bricked.

Hard bricked devices on the other hand are what mobile phone technicians generally regard as "dead phone". No sign of activity or life. The phone becomes absolutely non-responsive no matter what the user does, despite having adequate operating battery power. Hard bricking could also result from software related faults which can be traced to any of the following;

- Wrong selection of firmware for installation or flashing.
- Interruptions during the flash process.
- Wrong keypad code command syntax.
- Software bugs.
- Using a wrong flash procedure than recommended by the repair software manufacturer.

IMEI

IMEI is a short term for, International Mobile Equipment Identity, a unique 15-digit international serial number used to identify a mobile phone on a mobile phone network. This number can be used to identify illegal or stolen mobile phone devices. Whenever a mobile device is switched ON or a call is made on it, the network provider's switch checks the IMEI number of the handset and then cross references it with a blacklist database. If that IMEI is on the blacklist then the network will either block signals to the phone or allow signals but block outgoing or incoming calls. IMEI's importance is such that if it is missing, wrong, or corrupted, there will be no network service in the mobile device.

Flashing

Flashing is a process whereby existing firmware or data in a mobile phone's EEPROM or flash memory is overwritten with a fresh firmware code or new data. This can be done to upgrade a device, repair or fix bugs, swap a mobile service provider for network locked devices or just to install a new operating system. Some manufacturers like Apple for instance require over the air upgrades whereby the device is connected through the internet to the manufacturers' web server for the process.

Custom ROM/Stock ROM

Although ROM in computer terminology means Read Only Memory (A memory storage which once written, can neither be edited nor deleted), in Android OS community parlance it means firmware for Android phones and tablets. Changing or installing a ROM in a phone is similar to installing a new operating system on a desktop or laptop computer.

Android is an open source software which is supported by a vast community of developers that continually modify the code by adding features, customizations, and improvements to its stability and the product is what is referred to as Custom ROM.

Custom ROMs are replacement firmware for Android devices created by third-party software developers which provides features or options not found in the Stock (the device manufacturer's) OS. Custom ROMs are often built from the official files of Android or kernel source code. Examples of popular Custom ROMs are CyanogenMod, Paranoid Android, MIUI, and AOKP (Android Open Kang Project) etc.

Stock ROMs on the other hand are the Android firmware installed by the original equipment manufacturers (OEMs) in smartphones, running the Android mobile operating system. The companies customize and brand the phones to give it a unique look and feature that is proprietary. For instance, a Samsung phone and an LG phone just purchased off the shelf may be running the same version of Android OS. But when you switch both phones ON, each one would display their company brand name and the desktop environment may look different, with different widgets, wallpapers etcetera and even accompanying third-party apps.

Rooting

Rooting is a process that provides users with full administrator control and access to an Android smartphone or tablet. This is often done in order to bypass carrier or handset-maker limitations or restrictions. The moment a phone is rooted, applications and system settings can be replaced or modified, and specialized apps can be run and so on. Root access compromises device's user data security.

One major reason to root a phone is to replace the operating system with a ROM (ROM in this sense means another software developer's version of the OS) that also gives a user more control over key applications details. This process is commonly referred to as *flashing a custom ROM*.

The process of rooting an Android phone is different for each device and that is why this book can only point you to online resource links specific for each model of smartphone or tablet as long as you have understood the concept. Simply stated, if you want to root a phone, check the model number and manufacturer, search for the rooting procedure specific to that model and the software tool for it online and you will get it.

Other advantages of rooting include;

- Rooting provides the ability to uninstall (rather than disable) any unwanted apps and games that are preinstalled in phones which take up enormous storage space even though they are rarely used.
- Rooting enables faster platform updates. Custom ROMs can be flashed to access new released features once a device is rooted.
- Rooting makes available additional optional settings and control.

- Rooting a phone makes it possible to install new apps, gain more device management options and additional security functionality more than what is possible with the usual Android stock OS.

Note that when a phone is rooted, warranty becomes void; however, flashing a stock ROM can reverse the warranty status to original state. Few examples of apps that add new levels of functionality to a rooted Android phone include ROM Toolbox Pro, SetCPU, Titanium Backup, Touch Control, and Cerberus anti-theft and so on. So if you want to root a phone, not to worry. Here is a link to where you can find easy step-by-step guides for different models;

http://www.androidcentral.com/root

Phone Updates

Updating a phone simply means downloading firmware or OS files of higher versions with either bug fixes or add-ons and features into the device. Updating a phone's software reduces its internal storage as the new software instructs the phone to create more storage space designated for system use. Oftentimes updates to smartphones results into slower speed and responsiveness in phones which is actually a tradeoff for using older hardware to gain enhanced features meant for newer versions of hardware. While it seems impossible to manipulate the "read only" memory part of the phone using end user tools, it is possible using developer tools.

Read/Write/Update/Download

Various flasher box software interfaces use different language choices on their radio buttons. Apart from "read" which is usually for reading files and information from the phone, the rest (write, update, upload) are meant to transfer the firmware files from the computer into the device being flashed.

Android ADB driver

This (Android Debug Bridge) is a small application which auto installs in the computer to support all android devices that may be connected to the system for firmware flashing or any other operation including models like Samsung, Google Nexus, Xiaomi, Motorola, HTC, LG, Infinix, Tecno or other MTK phones, Huawei etc.

Download the "15 seconds ADB Installer" from;

http://androidmtk.com/download-bst-android-adb-driver. This installer was created by XDA developer "Snoop05".

USB DFU.exe

DFU stands for Download Firmware Utility or Device Firmware Update and as the name implies it can be used to flash both stock and custom ROMs of android smartphones and tablets especially for Broadcom android devices.

In iPhones, DFU mode is usually the mode of last resort when all other effort to recover the phone into a normal state fails. DFU mode in this case, different from "recovery mode" puts the device into communication with iTunes on a Windows® computer, although the boot loader or iOS has not been loaded yet, allowing the device to be recovered from any state.

Booting, Bootloader and the Booting Process

No human being falls asleep instantly and neither does anyone wake up from sleep in an instant, fully conscious and active 100%. Sleeping and waking is a process. Machines tend to be built as imitations of nature and God's creation. Therefore, booting is the initialization process of computing systems such as smartphones and tablets or PDAs.

Whenever a computer system assumes its normal operational runtime environment, ready to accept inputs to process and produce outputs, booting has been completed. If the booting process began from an OFF state to normal operational state, this can be regarded as "Hard booting". Soft booting is when the system boots up from a partially OFF state like hibernation, standby mode or sleeping mode.

A **boot loader** is a tiny, separate proprietary program or code resident in ROM or Flash memory as part of the firmware which is designed to automatically load an operating system into the main (working) memory of the computer and run it after completion of the power-on self-tests (POST).

But before the bootloader loads an Operating system image, it usually carries out an authentication check to ascertain the genuineness of the OS and a Cyclic Redundancy Check (CRC) to check errors. One way of doing this is by reading the boot partition's unique OEM (Original Equipment manufacturer) key's digital signature. If it is not digitally signed, the boot process fails. This OEM key is an encrypted unique code assigned to every manufacturer. Therefore, before any custom ROM can be installed on an Android phone, the bootloader must be unlocked.

Fastboot tool or specialized flasher devices are tools that unlock the bootloader of various phones during flashing.

In a computer system, the operating system is resident in secondary

Memory such as the Hard disk drive, HDD. Embedded systems like mobile phones however do not have such large storage space and are designed to boot fast, almost immediately after power ON. Therefore, such devices usually have operating system software or firmware in ROM or flash memory, so that the device can begin to function with little or no loading as the loading process can be pre-computed and stored on the ROM when the device is made. This is where basically the boot sequence of a computer desktop/laptop differs from that of a mobile device. The boot sequence for mobile devices' CPUs or DSPs (Digital Signal Processors) or microcontrollers (SoC- Socket on Chips) usually include a boot ROM with boot code integrated directly into their IC. This allows their processor to perform self-boot and load-boot programs from other sources like NAND flash, SD or eMMC etc. This feature is often used for system recovery purposes when the usual boot software in non-volatile memory gets erased or corrupted.

It is therefore possible to take control of a system by using hardware debug interfaces such as JTAG, connected to flasher boxes to write (unlock) the bootloader program before installing custom ROM into bootable non-volatile flash memory by instructing the processor core to perform the necessary actions needed to program non-volatile memory.

Mobile phones' (especially smartphone) processors are designed with multiple cores. In a dual core processor or instance, there is a master-slave relationship, where the DSPs' boot initialization is controlled by the CPU or Application processor (the Master) which boots first from its own memories and then controls overall system behavior - booting of the DSP - and other functional roles in the system. The DSP in most cases does not have its own boot memories, consequently relying on the master processor to initialize.

An Overview on Memory Modules and Processing Cores

The most critical components of a smartphone or tablet's architecture are the main memory modules, processing cores and the dedicated graphics processors.

RAM (Random Access Memory) or dynamic RAM (DRAM) is the primary memory of any computing system, without which file access and processing would be a drag or absolute failure. However, unlike in PCs where it is usually removable and expandable through slots, DRAM in smartphones and tablets are securely fixed (soldered) chips on the circuit board.

DRAM aids the processing cores with their processing activities by making data and files readily available to the processors. Critical files such as application data, operating system components, user data, file system in ROM or just about any file or data that must go through processing speedily, are first loaded into DRAM, awaiting execution or processing by the

CPU or other processors. The contents of DRAM are volatile, meaning that they can be changed quickly and easily to store different files. The volatility of DRAM or RAM is evident once there is a power failure or the phone is restarted, all the contents of the RAM (Apps that were in use, files that were open, processes that were running etc.) vanishes, unlike the flash memory or ROM storage which retains its contents. Information from the slower ROM or NVRAM (Non-volatile RAM) must be passed to the much faster RAM before reaching the processing cores and back.

As a hardware technician, understand that RAM is usually soldered on the circuit board close to the main processors or SoCs, not farther apart for the purpose of efficiencies. RAM is often placed directly on the SoC in what is called package-on-package (PoP) to enable direct access to the RAM and reduce power consumption or heat dissipation. Where a CPU, GPU or SoC is soldered on one side of the board, if you check on the reverse side, you find another chip (RAM) directly opposite these processing cores. Even if not placed in this kind of arrangement, it is usually soldered within close proximity to the processing cores.

RAM comes in different sizes and types, determining the performance levels recorded by the phone. For instance, there are descriptions such as SDRAM (Synchronous Dynamic Random Access Memory) or DDR SDRAM which means Double Data Rate Synchronous Dynamic Random Access Memory. Smartphones mostly use the LP DDR where LP stands or Low Power. Whether DDR or LP, once there is a specified suffix number, it signifies its generation. For instance, DDR1, DDR2, DDR3 and so on for generation 1, 2 and 3 respectively. To view these details about a device's number of cores or RAM and general details, install the app CPU-Z or the more detailed CPU-X from the Google Playstore. Then information gleaned from the apps comes handy when the phone is disassembled, using a microscope the tiny information usually inscribed on the chips (ICs) found on the mainboard can serve for proper identification of each chip.

By now you are familiar with ROM. ROM or internal storage provides the space for storing the operating system and other critical files required for the functioning of the phone. Some current smartphones and tablets are built with multiple storage chips which can be broken into partitions for different purposes, including operating system storage, applications storage, system cache, system files, user files or data and so on.

Rouse Margaret's[17] defines a multi-core processor as "a computer processor on a single integrated circuit with two or more separate processing units, called cores, each of which reads and executes program instructions". This is the simplest and explicit definition I have encountered about Multi-Core processing.

It is all about parallel processing of data simultaneously to increase speed, agility and responsiveness of computing devices, a technique known as Multithreading. We have smartphones with eight cores or more. What this means is that several CPU instructions like add, move, swipe, branch and so on can be simultaneously executed across each of those other processing cores in the same embedded Integrated Circuit.

The screenshots above are from my Samsung Galaxy A10 Tablet. Clearly written is its eight cores under the heading, CPU (Central Processing Unit). Other details of importance in the repair process are there, like the GPU type (MALI-G71), version of OS running – Android v9 (Pie) which is also very important to know when flashing a phone. It is better to flash an upgrade rather than downgrade version which will result in a "dead phone".

Sometimes a phone can be brought to a technician which is an imitation of the original brand cloned by any of the Chinese companies. This CPU-X information can help to confirm an original from a fake. One way the hardware names given can help is when working on a particular mainboard, like this A10 tablet for instance, sighting "MALI" on an IC chip would make it obvious it is the GPU. The CPU-X interface has many other features including testing the various peripheral components.

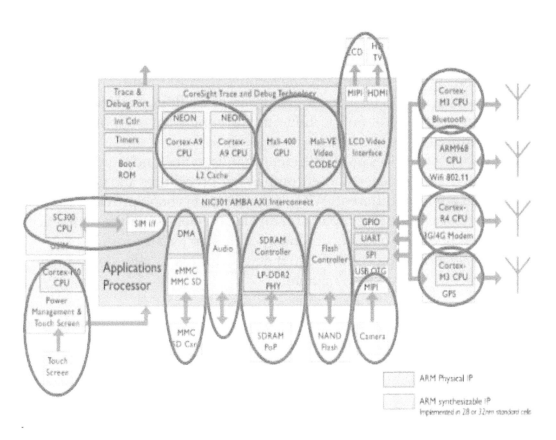

Image Credit: http://www.arm.com

Android smartphones first embraced the ARM processors in 2008, beginning the gradual evolution into the multi-core design with ARM Cortex A15, to Snapdragon developed by Qualcomm, SoCs and now Multi-core designs.

The Flash Programming Process

Up to this point, having learnt about the various ways phone software faults manifests or a phone becomes bricked as well as the causes or sources of bricking in a mobile device, we shall now examine the procedures and processes involved in proffering solutions to bricked phones through flash programming.

Flashing as has been defined in this book is simply a process whereby a technician uses phone flasher devices and software to reload a new, updated, valid firmware or operating system into a bricked mobile device thereby replacing the corrupted one.

It is also important that every detail of the structure of the phones, their memories and the relationship with the microprocessors is both understood and internalized in memory. Note that Flash programming operations cannot take place if any of either the *Flash memory, microprocessors, data communication ports* or the *power management IC* of the phone is faulty. These hardware components must first be functional and **properly soldered** to the PCB. For this reason, during a flash operation, the technician must intuitively monitor the communications from the flasher box program's output on the computer screen and respond to error notifications, interpreting what component is affected accordingly.

Phone flashers or devices are of different brands, types, and support levels. Here we shall learn the general all-encompassing procedures and concepts although each device is different. What is taught in this book provides the latitude to approach software repairs for any smartphone or tablet in practice, even if there is one or two unique, brand-specific step (as an addition or omission to the general procedures listed here) which is usually stated in the flasher maker's user instruction manual.

The Flash Procedure

The following steps must be completed by a technician who wants to flash a mobile device;

✓ Download and install all the required **drivers** for both the phones and the flasher boxes to be used on the computer system. Phone driver software is required mostly for any standalone repair software that is only installed in the computer without an authentication flasher box interface to enable it for use. However, if a flasher box is being used for flashing, various phone model's drivers are not required to be installed first on the computer system because they are included with the setup installation files accompanying the flasher box.

✓ Download and install **setup files** for the flasher boxes on the computer system. Most setup files include the device drivers for the phone brands and models the flasher box supports.

✓ Install the flasher device. Each device follows a laid out routine. In most cases they follow a similar device installation pattern. Study the installation routine in the next section of this book.

✓ Download and install the repair software suite for specific flasher boxes you want to use on the computer system.

✓ Download, extract and label appropriately (in individual folders for each mobile device model) the mobile device's firmware files or flash files on the computer system. Flash files used for some specific flasher boxes are unique to those flasher boxes and available only in their support websites and GSM forums. If you do not purchase a valid legitimate branded flasher box from the manufacturer's authorized resellers, you will not be able to gain access to support areas to download flash-files and other useful resources. However, some files can be used across flasher boxes 'platforms.

Having completed all software and hardware device installations needed for the repair flash programming process, the technician will need to understand each **repair software's** user interface parameters;

- Functions of the radio buttons
- Communication port settings
- The Flash processes' sequence and timing for certain user actions (e.g. a button that must be pressed at specific timeframe, say "X" number of seconds after pressing the "Flash" or "Update" or "Unlock" or "Start" or whatever actionable code command button.)
- Flash file 'Type' selection

Once the above-listed parameters are known and understood, the flash process is easy and straight forward. Just click on the button marked any of "Flash/Write/Update Firmware/Download" etc. depending on whatever language was used on the software interface that represents "flash" or unlock.

Other parameters that constitute actionable command operations are;

- Write Operations (IMEI, Phonebook, Full Flash, PM)
- Factory Settings
- Format
- Read Operations (Flash, IMEI, Lock Code or Security Code, Phonebook, Gallery)
- Erase (Full Flash, Security Areas, etc) and so on.

The repair interface programs are usually designed with multi-view window tabs that grant access to the user to execute a whole lot of programming options possible with the flasher box used.

Fastboot Android Protocol

Fastboot is a protocol as well as a tool used for diagnostics purposes in Android phones. Developers integrated the Fastboot protocol into Android devices' software development kit (SDK), although some may not have it. As a protocol, it defines a communication process that puts the phone into bootloader or Secondary Loader mode, giving access into the device such that custom images (software codes) can be written into the various disk partitions of the Android device by connecting the phone through USB to the computer. It could be recovery.img files, system.img file, logo.img etc.
As a tool, the Fastboot tool when used provides a command-line interface through which a user can modify, wipe or load those images into the phone.
    In order to use the Fastboot tool to perform diagnostic operations on a phone, the phone must be put in Fastboot mode through a combination of keys on the phone. For example, the POWER + VolumeUP or VolumeDOWN and Home button keys in some phones or just POWER + VolumeDOWN or UP. After enabling the protocol on the device itself, it will accept a specific set of commands sent to it via USB using a command line. Some of the most commonly used fastboot commands include:

- **Flash** – rewrites a partition with a binary image stored on the host computer. Syntax is; "fastboot flash <type of file-name> {space}<name of file>"
- **Erase** – erases a specific partition. Syntax is; "fastboot erase <type of file-name or partition name>
- **Format** – formats a specific partition; the file system of the partition must be recognized by the device. Syntax is; "fastboot format <partition-name>".

- **Unlock/Lock** – For unlock/relock of bootloader. Syntax is; "Fastboot oem unlock" and "fastboot oem lock".

Most Android-based smartphones have a procedure through which the device can be placed into this mode in order to execute commands through user interface flash tools created for that purpose.

Also, **most** direct USB flash tool software programs (i.e. no flasher box connected between phone and computer; just USB cable and the software installed on the computer) require that the user puts the device into a specific mode before the flash software can execute flash/unlock/format or other service operations on the mobile device.

China Phones Software Repairs

China phones refer to a group and type of phones under certain identified platforms based on the base microprocessor technologies used for manufacturing these smartphones and tablets. MediaTeK (MTK) processors are the most popular featured brand common with China phones.

MediaTeK is a popular chip manufacturing company based in Taiwan that mostly outsources their products, and their largest demands come from the Chinese mobile technology market.
There are other notable base chips in China phones as was listed in the F.A.Q earlier. For instance, for iTEL Spreadtrum (SPD) MCUs, you need to use Research Download software, which is a free tool as well.

SP Flash tool remains relevant today as it were four years ago as an Android flashing software tool. However, Flasher boxes though usually packing specialized powerful phone repair features for various brands oftentimes trend over a period of time as new ones debut with greater improvements just as new smartphones and tablets are being manufactured. So for a book like this which will be around for decades, name dropping or recommendation of specifics is impractical. This book and the first edition will continue to be of help to many people, many years into the future, for mastering basic to advanced technical phone repairs knowledge, relevant even in future technologies. For instance, where will Miracle box or Infinity box be in say 10 years' time? That, I cannot predict. But there will always be new flasher box products for all generations.

To carry out software repairs, update or upgrade of China phones, the technician should use any of the current software flasher boxes alongside direct USB, using MTK/SP flash tool software. There is **MTK flash tool** for china feature phones while **SP flash tool** is for china Smartphones.

To flash using SP flash tool;

- You need the USB cable to connect the phone to the computer.
- You need the USB drivers for each phone you are connecting to the computer to be detected correctly.
- You also need the Custom ROM or firmware file for each phone downloaded into a folder.
- Then you should download (it is <u>freely</u> available online in different versions) the SP flash tool as well as a USB DFU.exe file. Use the USB dfu.exe file to remove or uninstall previous drivers from the system.
- Open the computer system's device manager;
- Connect the USB cable to the phone you want to flash with a custom ROM without battery (some may require battery);
- Once you connect, you should see MTK preloader; Right click on it and select "update Driver". A pop-up menu appears as below;

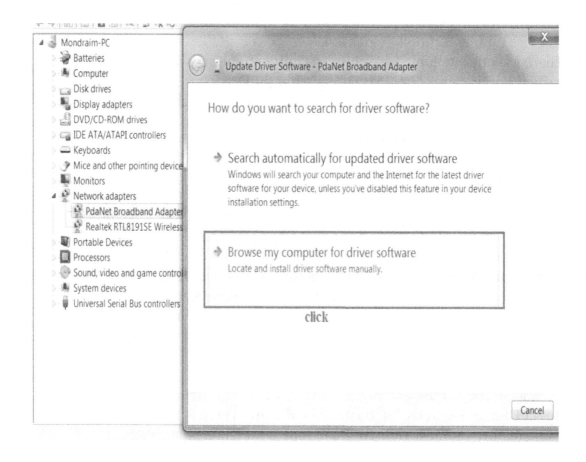

- Select "Browse my computer for driver software" and point to the folder where you saved the phone's driver. Be sure you select the right folder that matches your Windows version.
- When you select the driver you might get a message that the driver is not digitally signed; therefore, you might have to disable driver signature enforcement by;

  i. Rebooting the computer

  ii. Pressing "F8" continually until a screen appears as below

  iii. Select "Disable Driver Signature Enforcement"

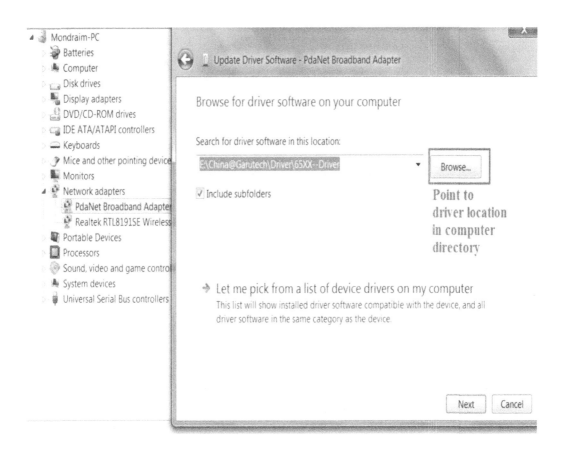

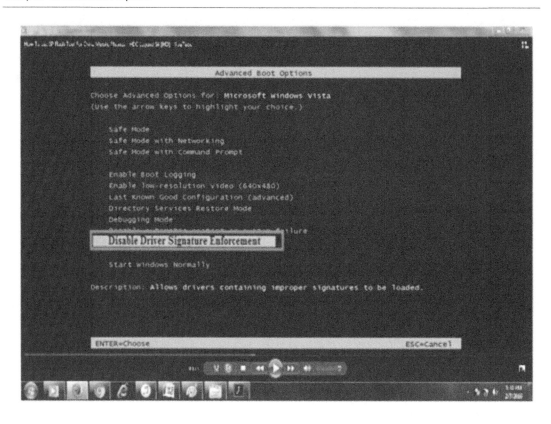

- Now back to the flashing process; ensure the custom ROM you want to flash is extracted into a folder. For instance here is a Tecno H6 file.

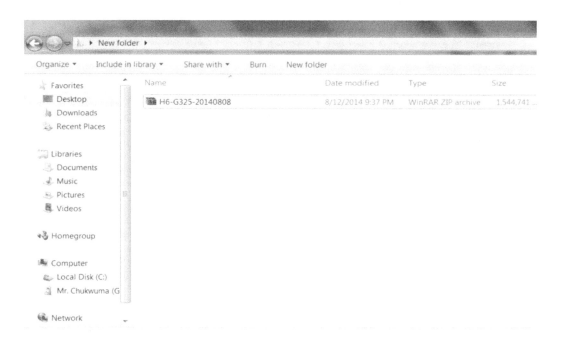

- Right click and select "extract here" option

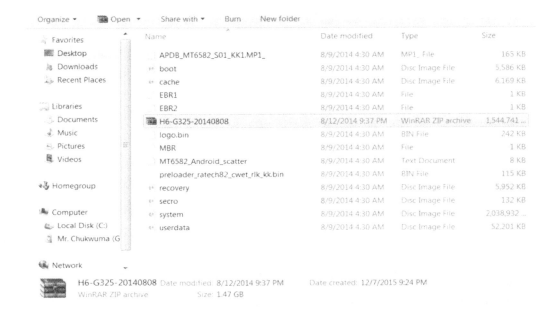

- You can see all the files extracted. The one, of importance which you will point to later as you click "Scatter loading" below is the "scatter.txt" file. Select the file "**MT6582_Android_scatter**" as seen in the screen shot below circled in red;

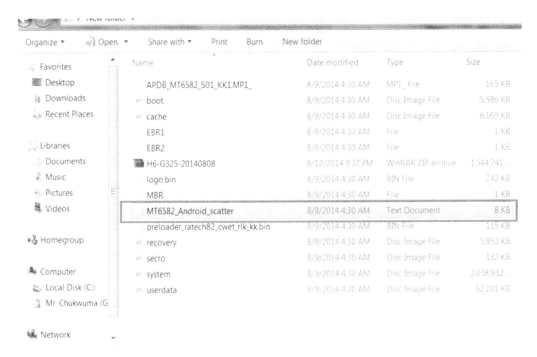

- Next, run the SP flash tool program and click on "scatter loading". You might notice that the "Scatter.txt" file is only 8kb in size. It is normal. The scatter file only helps to aggregate together all the partition component files required for flashing.

    The main files run into gigabytes in size. Therefore, don't let the small file size bother you.

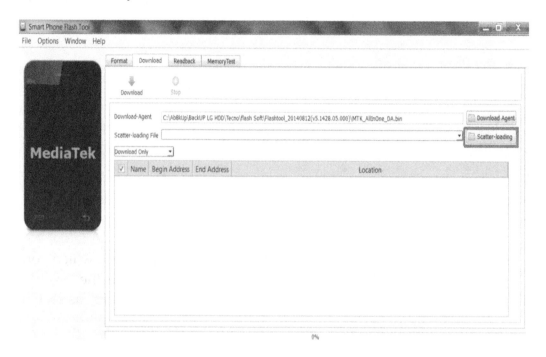

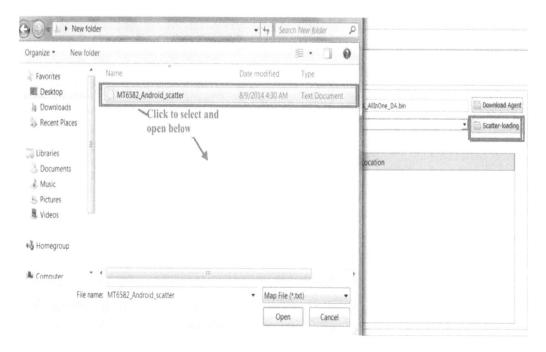

The Android scatter file contains information about the device's structure with the memory map of the image file, and loads all the flash file components into the flash tool in preparation for the flash process.

The Android smartphone's NVRAM is basically like a hard drive consisting of several partitions. While one of those partitions holds the Android system files, another holds all the app data accumulated by users and others for backend processing by the phone. Note that all the files required are check-marked and has a file path to indicate their location in the computer system. If you do not want to flash a particular file, for instance "Recovery", just uncheck the selection of that particular file. The list includes;

i.   **PRELOADER** – Specific to each device and must be present in every custom ROM extract or the phone cannot enter download mode. The preloader communicates with the computer during flashing by making the phone to be detected as a port which should be flash-able. Downloading a wrong pre-loader can brick a phone. If not needed, never flash the preloader (Do not check-mark it)

ii.   **MBR** – Master Boot Record (first sector of any partitioned drive which invokes Volume Boot Record that holds the boot code)

iii.   **EBR1** – Internal memory storage partition for apps installation (2GB)

iv.   **BOOT.IMG** – Boot code file partition for device booting. boot.img contains the kernel and RAMdisk, critical files necessary to load the device before the file system can be mounted

v.   **UBOOT** – Universal Bootloader

vi.   **Recovery** - It contains the recovery system as an alternative boot partition that lets the device boot into a recovery console for performing advanced recovery and maintenance operations on it.

vii.   **SEC_RO** – Important file for IMEI write/repair and the Baseband processor.

viii.   **LOGO** – Boot logo

ix.   **EBR2** – Phone storage which acts as Memory card if no memory card is installed (6GB). Once a memory card is installed, it becomes a dormant, wasted memory space. It can be reconfigured to benefit a client user, freeing up more memory storage space.

x.   **Android** – Android OS partition for system image

xi. **Cache** - This partition stores frequently accessed data and app components. It is an internal memory temporary storage.

xii. **USER_DATA** - This partition contains user's data like contacts, SMS, settings etc. Factory reset on a device usually clears this partition.

- Once everything is checked, next is to click "Download" button. There are other options in the drop-down menu beneath "scatter-loading file" such as "Format All + Download", "Firmware Upgrade". They are controlled by the "Download" button if any option is chosen.

- After clicking on the download button, connect the phone (turned OFF state), without battery (in some cases with battery) to the computer. As soon as that is done, the flash process begins. It will take a while. Wait until a green circle appears, with "Download Ok" written.

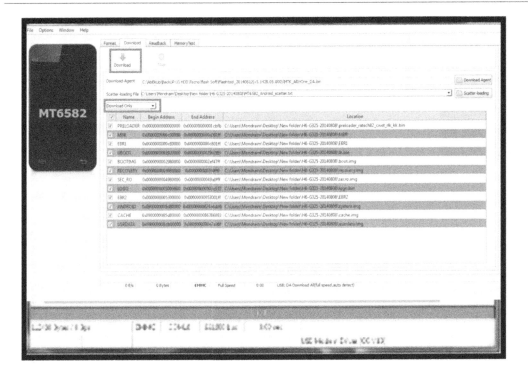

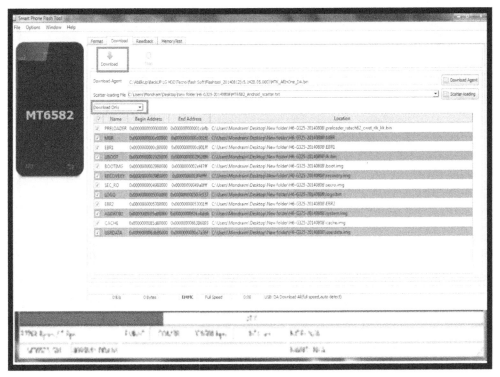

First you will see red horizontal stripe, then purple, yellow and then the green circle in that order.

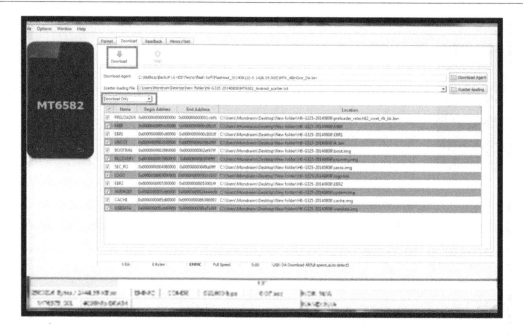

- After you see the green circle, next disconnect the phone from the system, attach the battery and press the Power ON button. It may take a little while to boot. Do not worry until it powers ON.

The process above is for flashing the whole custom ROM. If you want to flash just a part of the ROM, just deselect all other check-marked items in the scatter loaded list above. There are times you may need to format first, before flashing the ROM.

Warning: Always make sure that you trust the sources of the ROM meant for the phone being flashed because flashing a wrong preloader will kill the phone. It will become completely dead (neither power ON, charge nor be detected by the computer) and recovery is almost impossible. Be careful!

Flashing Samsung Phones

From the table of flasher boxes in Table 8.1, a technician can select any or all of the support tool boxes that support Samsung flashing/unlock. But for the purposes of helping a start-up technician, who may not have ready cash to invest in tool boxes, let me walk through a simple tutorial on how to use the Odin software just like I did with the SP Flash tool tutorial.

The Odin software is a support tool from Samsung originally meant to be used exclusively in Samsung support offices.

Ok, let us do a quick rundown.

i.   You have a Laptop or desktop computer.
ii. You have USB cable for phone-to-computer communication.
iii. You have a Samsung phone that is bricked.
iv. You want to flash or reload the Operating system/firmware.

The next items you need are;

i.   Samsung firmware files for that particular model of Samsung you want to flash. Go online and download the firmware flash-files. **Find links in the "Resource Links" section at the end of the book**

ii. Odin software. There are many versions of Odin software. Find an up-to-date version.

The components of the Samsung firmware files on the software interface, depending on the version of Odin being used are;

a. AP file (Modem file); type .MD5
b. BL file; type .MD5
c. CP file; type .MD5
d. CSC file; type .MD5
e. A file name (varies); type .pit file
f. PDA button is for the main software in older versions of Odin
g. Phone button for Modem files in older version of Odin
h. Bootloader for new bootloader files

The Pit files will only be needed if firmware updates needs to change the phone's partition layout which is rarely required. But if the partition table is corrupted, .pit file will be required. Do not bother about using the pit file except as needed. *Select files according to the radio buttons seen on the software interface, that is, click on each respective file name's button and match it with selecting the file name on the computer folder.*

Before the Flash Process

a. Ensure that your computer system has Samsung Kies installed which enables Samsung device drivers in the system.

b. After installation of Samsung Kies, close the application, download and install the Odin.exe software.

The Flash Process

To begin the flash process;

a. The firmware files extracted into a folder need to be selected one after the other by clicking on the respective buttons on the software interface.

b. After selecting the files, next is to put the phone into download mode by pressing some key combinations. Turn the phone off and then press simultaneously the VolumeDown + Home button + Power button. A pop up warning sign will appear with options; "Press VolumeUP to continue OR VolumeDown to cancel". Press volume up and it will put the phone in download mode.

c. Run the Odin software to begin.

d. On the software interface, ensure these two options are check-marked; "Auto Reboot" and "F.Reset Time".

e. Plug the mobile phone into the computer. Allow time for the drivers to install and then wait for the section "ID: COM" on the software interface to change to the color blue.

f. Press start to begin the flash process. As soon as the process begins, do not remove the USB cable or turn OFF the computer or any other form of disruption.

g. After the flash process has ended, the phone will reboot. If the software experiences hang/freeze during this operation, you may detach and re-attach the USB cable and Odin should continue the process.

Flash Procedure for iPhones

iPhone runs on its proprietary iOS operating system. To flash an iPhone in order to fix software bugs, upgrades or install updates, the following procedures should suffice. Most software problems can be resolved by flashing with the iOS firmware.

1. Download and install iTunes which is apple's video management and playback software. This software is used for managing iOS devices, such as backing up data and restoring devices' OS.
2. Download the corresponding iPhone firmware. Ensure to match each iPhone model with its firmware and version. iTunes also verifies firmware version during the update process.
3. Connect iPhone to PC / Mac with a cable, usually same USB cable used for charging the device.
4. Automatically the phone checks for compatible system drivers. Once the driver update is completed, the iPhone will vibrate with a sound or beep. After successful connection, iTunes will prompt to allow access to iPhone information. Select "trust" on the iPhone to permit communication between it and the system.

NEXT, in the iTunes software, go to iPhone interface;

If using a Windows PC: Press "shift" button and click "Check for update / Restore iPhone" simultaneously.
If using a Mac PC: Hold down the "option" button and click "Check for update / Restore iPhone".

Also;

To save internal user data in the iPhone, select "update".
To erase all data in the iPhone, select "restore iPhone".

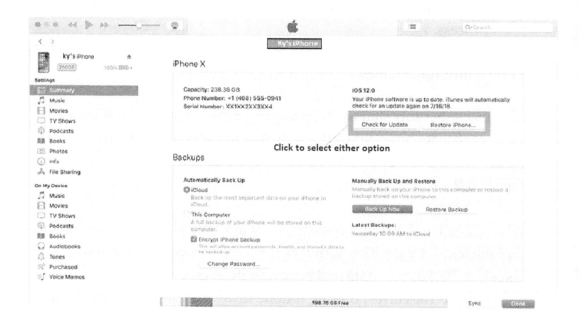

5. A notification pops up saying, "select the firmware". Select the downloaded firmware file and click "ok". Then select either "Check for update" or "Restore iPhone". Wait for a few minutes until the process is finished.

6. Then, restart the iPhone and use.

Method II: Using Recovery mode or DFU mode

This method is used when resolving;

a. Forgotten password issues
b. When iPhone is deactivated
c. Dead iPhone (power ON failure)

DFU is short for Development Firmware Upgrade. It is indicative of the forced upgrade or downgrade mode of iPhone firmware. The difference between iPhone recovery mode and DFU mode is only dependent on whether iBoot is activated. In recovery mode, iBoot is used to restore and upgrade the firmware while in DFU mode, the system does not activate iBoot. Sometimes, the firmware can be successfully downgraded in DFU mode.

To put iPhone 6s and older models into Recovery mode;

    a.   Turn off the iPhone, press and hold the home button for 3 seconds to connect it to the PC / Mac.

    b. Next, press and hold down the home button until the recovery mode appears. (iTunes icon will be displayed on the screen)

To put iPhone 6s and older models into DFU mode;

    a. First connect the iPhone to a PC or Mac.

    b. Press and hold the power button and the home button at the same time.

    c. Release the power button while the iPhone's screen is off after three seconds.

    d. iTunes will prompt "detect an iPhone is in recovery mode".

To put iPhone 7 into Recovery mode;

    a. Turn off the iPhone, press the volume down button for 3 seconds, and connect it to the PC / Mac.

    b. Then press the volume down button and the recovery mode appears. (iTunes icon is displayed on the screen)

To put IPhone 7 models into "DFU" mode

    a. Connect the iPhone to a PC / Mac.

    b. Press and hold the power button and the volume down button at the same time.

    c. When the iPhone screen is off for three seconds, release the power button (but don't release the volume down button).

    d. When the iTunes prompt "detect an iPhone in recovery mode", release the volume down button.

To put IPhone 8 or iPhone X models into "recovery mode"

    a. Press the volume up button, then press the volume down button, then press the power button.

    b. After the screen goes black, press the volume down button and the recovery mode appears (the iTunes icon is displayed on the screen).

To put iPhone 8 or iPhone X models into "DFU" mode

    a. Press the volume up button, then press the volume down button, and then press the power button.

    b. Release the power button after the screen goes black.

    c. Hold the power button and volume down button for 5 seconds simultaneously

   d. Then release the power button, and hold the volume down for 5 seconds.

   e. Enter the DFU mode.

   f. ITunes pops up recovery window, click "ok".

For PC users: Hold "shift" button and click "Restore iPhone".

For Mac users: Hold down "option" button and click "Restore iPhone" at the same time.

When "select firmware" notification pops up, select the downloaded firmware. Click "ok" and start updating. Wait for a few minutes until the iPhone finished the restore process.

NOTE: It is safe to carry out a backup of iPhone data before update. Also, during the update process, do not disconnect the iPhone to avoid irreparable damage.

Also, details of the flashing procedure for flasher devices was covered in the first edition, "Mobile Phones and Tablets Repairs: A Complete Guide for Beginners and Professionals".

Web Links to Useful Resources for Software Repairs

1. http://www.needrom.com for smartphone Custom ROMs
2. http://www.imeidata.net for confirming originality of a phone through its IMEI and then get the appropriate ROM for the phone.
3. http://www.phoneinfo.com to check a phone's status using IMEI
4. http://firmwarefile.com/walton-primo-f4b.d for ALL phone firmware files.
5. http://lg-firmware-rom.com for LG smartphones. Just type the phone's IMEI and its file appears.
6. https://www.androidmtk.com/download-lg-usb-drivers for LG Android drivers.
7. http://www.icloud.com/activationlock to check the icloud status of an iPhone.
8. http://forum.xda-developers.com/showthread.php?t=961956 for latest Samsung Android ADB drivers.
9. http://www.driverscape.com/download/cdc-serial for cdc-serial driver.
10. http://www.romkingz.com for custom ROMs of Android phones
11. http://www.hovatek.com for MTK ROM files support.
12. http://droidblaze.com.ng/2015/07/list-og-tecno-stock-roms-download-links.html to access links to Tecno files
13. http://forum.gsmhosting.com
14. http://www.google.com

Chapter 9

User Interface Settings and Codes

Incorporated into the menu system of phones is the "settings" option where each device provides users with the capability to set some user preferences on the device. Among these options is the ability to clear internal memory caches, reset the device to factory settings and so on. Recent Android OS versions now include an app known as "Device Care" which helps automate these actions at once.

However, there are also hidden code routines that resets the EEPROM or contents of the NVRAM or Flash memory. The latter is possible especially in some devices where the manufacturer loaded two copies of firmware. One is active while the other one is stored in ROM or flash memory where normal operating processes cannot corrupt the files. Then, they include a keyboard keys-combination activated hidden code routine which is reserved for only trained support personnel to use.

When activated, corrupted active version of firmware can be cleared by copying a stored copy of firmware over the active version as a replacement. In some other brands or models, a minimal bootloader firmware is designed to be enabled by an internal "reset switch or jumper" which when pressed can reload the main firmware. In some older phones, you must have noticed some phones or other devices that have a tiny pin-hole somewhere on the body which serves as a reset switch when pressed with a needle tip.

It is important that a technician understand the workings of these systems even if in very simplistic ways although great effort is made to help the reader achieve great proficiency in this practical book.

When the level of knowledge is in-depth, a great technician is in the making and that is the major purpose of this book. If it motivates the reader to dig deeper for knowledge on these topics, especially given the dynamics of technology over time, or to even pursue further formal education in electronics, what a joy!

Hard Reset is a manual method for formatting a device using keypad character combinations which deletes the device's user data in the internal memory. This is the same as factory reset or master reset. Hard reset does not affect data stored in the memory card. Hard-reset deletes all downloaded data saved in the phone which includes phone contacts, music files, pictures, videos, apps/app settings, SMS messages etc. Hard reset returns the phone back to its original settings and is also referred to as factory reset.

Soft Reset on the other hand is simply the act of power-cycling the mobile device which forces the clearing of the DRAM or Main memory (recall that it is a volatile memory that loses its contents when it loses power). This is necessary when the device hangs or freezes and become unresponsive.

To do this, just press the power-button continuously until the phone shuts down. Then reboot the device. This should be done before a hard reset is necessitated. Some phones have optional feature that allows ONLY reset of the phone settings without deleting user data. This option is also a soft reset routine and solves some settings related faults.

Warning: Never do a hard reset on any phone without adequate battery charge and be sure the client has no concern for data loss (who doesn't?). Where possible, create a backup first.

#*SECRET CODES*#

Never get carried away with secret codes! It is important to note that while they are handy tools sometimes, wrong application of an unverified code could lead to fatal consequences. Don't get scared. Just be cautious.

*#06#: To view ALL mobile phone's IMEI (International Mobile Equipment Identifier).

Samsung Phones

i.   *2767*3855# - EEPROM reset code that clears user locks, user data and minor memory errors that affect the normal operation of the phone.

ii.   *2767*3855# - Master EEPROM reset code that clears non-OS damaged faults.

Note: Be sure it is absolutely necessary before issuing this factory data reset command.

Other ways of resetting Samsung phones is through the settings menu. If it is possible to access the system menu, then;

➤ Select the settings option >'Backup and Restore'> 'Factory Data Reset'>'Reset Phone' and select "Yes" to confirm ERASE.

OR

➤ Switch off the mobile device.
➤ Press and hold the side Volume Up and Volume Down keys simultaneously or in some – Volume Up (or Volume Down) + Home button).
➤ Press and hold the Power button (now all 3 keys simultaneously) until the phone vibrates. Wait until the Android logo appears on screen. When it appears, release all the buttons.
➤ An options menu screen comes up –Navigate to "Wipe data/Factory reset" option using the volume down button. To select this option use the power button.
➤ Next, scroll down to "Delete all user data" using the volume down key and select it with the power button.
➤ The device will be formatted. Finally scroll to and select the option – "Reboot system now" using the power button. The process will start and complete in less than a minute and the phone will restart automatically.

*This works for Samsung Smartphones running on Android and **most Android smartphones and tablets of other brands and models**. These key combinations are important when access to the system menu is blocked by the prevailing fault. It is good to try these methods for any software related or lock issue before using a flasher or repair software solution. Note that some Samsung phones differ in the initial key combinations.*

Try any of the following;

➤ Power key + Volume Up + Volume Down **or**

➢ Power key + Volume Up + Home button **or**

➢ Power key + Volume Down + Home button

iii. *#0*# - check the screen clarity with this code in all Samsung phones including latest models.

iv. 0000, 000000 or 00000000 - Default Security Codes when prompted in security settings.

China Phone Models

China Basic/Feature phones

- To change phone language to English language, try *#0044# or *#001# and send.
- To set default language: type *#0000# Send.
- To enter the engineering mode, without SIM inserted, type*#3646633# send.
- To Reset defaults (phone/user code reset to default): *#9998*7328# (hold #).
- To Reset defaults (phone/user code reset to default): *01763*737381#.
- To Reset Factory settings ***000*.
- To unlock phone code, only press***847# without SIM card.

China Smartphones on Android

Apply any one combination of keys as stated below to open menu options;

➢ Power key + Volume Up + Home button OR

➢ Power key + Volume Down + Home button

➢ Power key + Volume UP + Volume Down

➢ Power key + Volume UP **Or** Volume Down

Once the Android logo appears, release the power button until the menu screen appears. Scroll to "wipe/Factory settings" and select using the power button. All the procedures described under Samsung apply too.

Chapter 10

Trade Secrets and Service Center Operational Guide

In real life, every business sector or industry has established sets of rules, codes of conduct and standard business practice guidelines for success. These informal and sometimes formal rules may be termed "secrets" whereas they are just part of the same universal ethos that governs practical living on earth.

To work is to live!

Don't get me wrong. There are hidden practices in some fields of endeavor that an uninitiated who ventures into such line of business without learning about them will fail. Experience as often said, is the best teacher. Therefore in concluding our lessons in this book, and based on practical experiences gathered over the years in offering technical support to various kinds of individuals, it is important to use those experiences to formulate a set of guides that would help a start-up technician avoid the mistakes and pitfalls of others before them, thereby leading to success.

Therefore, consider this section as a sort of business advisory and not as a cast iron rule that must apply.

The Purposeful Technician

Like every other vocation man is engaged in, there must be a vision backed by a purpose. Money shouldn't be the only overriding motivation.

Dr. Myles Munroe stated this most succinctly, that "if the purpose of a thing is not known, abuse is inevitable". The technician who wants to succeed must have a vision. It would be helpful for such a person to ask and answer some pertinent questions like the following;

Why do I want to do this job?

There must be a burning desire and interest behind offering technical service. One must see himself or herself as a "go-to" person whenever people face challenges. In the employment market, it is what is known as a solution provider or someone possessing "problem-solving skills". One must be consumed with the hunger to be the solution others are seeking, to technical issues. Such a person must not be irritated by any kind of persons, but like a medical doctor, be ready to deal patiently with all persons. To be effective, one must have a sense of adequate compensation (not greed) for offering the best service necessary.

Why this particular line of business?

There must be a sort of desire to belong to a certain professional group. Every profession in the world has an imitation. Every good product as well has the fake or substandard equivalent. What kind of professional one chooses to be, is dependent on that person's world view. It does not matter what anyone does to make money and be counted as successful; what matters is the responsible pursuit of excellence. Be a master in deed not on paper. Observe that every vocation on earth, whether rated low or high has produced successful men.

Success is a personal choice. *Therefore to be a technical support personnel who attracts men and women of all cadres, class and financial status, especially one entrusted with people's private information storage device such as a smartphone or tablet, places one in the corridor of power!*

What is done with such power is up to the technician. Be responsible!

Where do I want to be, in say, the next five years?

There must also be a plan towards an end. Every business is an investment vehicle. In order to travel from city A to city B, oceans apart for instance, a man would arrive city B only after utilizing several means of transport. This is similar to businesses and the journey of life.

Therefore to succeed, your final vision must be the driving-force for your performance in the present preoccupation which is Smartphones and

Tablets repairs.

The Character for Entrepreneurial Success

Truth is, an expert in any field of work can fail miserably in life and business if lacking in good character. A good technician should possess the following character traits for success. They include but not limited to the following;

- Discipline
- Integrity
- Persistence
- Capacity
- Honesty
- Patience
- Courtesy
- Resourcefulness

Discipline: You need discipline to excel. It is discipline that drives you to the workshop early in the morning and keeps you in your position until closing hours without being distracted by any other concern than to attend to and meet your customer's needs. Operate like an established corporate organization. Even though you are the only staff, imbibe the corporate culture for success. This discipline begins from day one - whether the patronage has begun or not.

Integrity: Integrity is more precious than gold. It is your integrity which is at play in the way and manner you handle client's devices that will announce you to others. It is your integrity that will drive some clients to offer you greater business benefits aside your primary technical support services' compensation. Don't think no one is taking notice – indeed its fragrance is everywhere around you.

For instance, never exchange one component from Mr. A's device with that of MR. B's with the justification that at a later time, you will purchase a replacement. It is not the same thing. Respect your client's device's components because the quality and lifecycle of one part differs from another. Respect also the privacy of their data. This is absolutely very important. When you do so, although in secret, there is that invisible helping force that is all-seeing who will withdraw his help towards your business.

Never sacrifice your integrity on the altar of expediency!

Persistence: A technician should not be someone who gives up easily. In fact, success knows no man who easily gives up in life. In proffering solutions to mobile devices, you must persist and get it done or you lose a great market share to your competitors.

Capacity: Without both mental and technical capacity, the technician will almost function in a manner akin to a robot. What this means is, only the knowledge gained at the time of training is that technician's currency of capacity. This is wrong. Keep abreast of knowledge-online and offline. Learn every day and be creative.

Honesty: The technician must be honest, no matter the circumstance. Earn what is due to you but be honest. There is no universal pricing policy. To do this, you must be clever enough to differentiate between information to be shared, not to be shared and how to share it to your clients.

Patience: Without patience, one is prone to giving up easily. Be patient by applying diligence. Impatience leads to the loss of other virtues including those listed above.

Courtesy: It is often said that the customer is king. Above all things treat them with utmost respect. However do not be bullied into losing your personal self-esteem. If your conduct is guided by what you have read so far, you would at most be in the right always. But yet, be courteous and create a respectful work environment that will pave way for mutual trust - and trust brings quality patronage.

Resourcefulness: A technical solution provider must have an uncanny ability to cope with unusual or difficult situations. Every day in a workshop is different, presenting the technician with different devices' fault challenges. If you hate monotonous jobs, this is a great place to test your love for variety and excellence.

Useful Work Routine Guides and Customer Service

Below are some tips to serve as operating principles specifically for mobile phone technical support technicians. It is important to learn the proper steps to take when faced with the following;

- The task of troubleshooting and repair of a mobile phone
- Billing a customer
- Time management

- Dealing with troublesome clients
- General service center operational routines

The task of troubleshooting and repair of a mobile phone

Whenever a faulty device is brought to the "Mobile Phone Service Centre" (to be referred to in this teaching as MPSC), as a solution provider, believe that every problem can be solved and receive the device.

Do not be intimidated by any of the following;

- ✓ The personality of the client.
- ✓ The sophistication of the mobile device.
- ✓ The complexity of the reported fault.

If you were not competent, neither of these listed factors would have permitted the challenge to be directed your way. *Be confident.* Why?

i.   It will inspire your client to retain your services.
ii. You will negotiate better financial compensation for almost the same repair routines because all devices are first and foremost ELECTRONIC devices!

Fault manifestations are usually different in nature, so never expect to have seen it all. *Never inspect or attempt repairs on a device in the presence of clients.* Why?

i.   It is unprofessional especially where a device is of a very high sophistication or complexity to you - this is relative. Another technician who might have handled a similar phone and issue will see it as a common fault. It is unprofessional because due to the pressure of prying eyes, you might be forced to take a wrong action that required a relaxed, studious observation before action.
ii. It reduces your capacity to negotiate adequate compensation. (There are cases where this works in the reverse – (where some braggadocio in front of the client intimidates for benefit and such a device must be one that the technician knows its intricacies like the back of his palm).

Be clear about the client's complaints, the current general status of the device, the clients' expectations, and what you agreed to render as a service. Why?

i.   To avoid unnecessary bickering and quarrels within your business environment. One incident will rub your business wrongly no matter your level of excellence.

ii.   Document the transaction contract.

iii.   Carry out a thorough visual inspection on the device and point out any abnormality if observed.

Ask relevant questions about the device's history before and after the fault occurred. Why?

i.   It is a very quick way for fault prognosis (A forecast of the outcome due to an earlier cause based on your technical knowledge). Ask questions like "what happened before the fault? Is it a reoccurring phenomenon? Is it a victim of liquid spillage? Did it experience heavy impact on a hard surface? Did it just occur spontaneously without a user's action?" These are questions that help to establish possible causes of failure and areas of focus for repair.

ii.   To protect your integrity in case of buck passing in case the device may have passed through previous wrong technical procedures.

Based on knowledge, determine mentally, the distinction between a software and hardware fault before billing the client. Why?

As you have learned in this book, there are software repairs and hardware repairs. Each type of repair procedure factors into the eventual cost of repairs. To buttress this point, let us see some few determinant observation checks;

✓ A broken, blank, white or cracked LCD screen needs to be determined as a hardware or software issue. Observe if the device can power "ON" by any noticeable activity like lighting, keypad or ring tones on it, call reception and transmission etc. These are signs of LCD problem which is hardware. If not consider software repairs.

✓ When there are partially responsive or totally unresponsive keys, then a hardware or software related Keypad Malfunction issue is at hand. Usually it is a hardware fault though.

✓ When the phone consistently restarts (auto-reboot) or automatically turns off; on a scale of 10, 8 is software related while 2 is hardware fault.

✓ Or the phone is stuck on logo only, without responding while in use or running any application. That, is a software problem.

The above listed are not exhaustive; but enough to drive home the point I am making. Also note that over time in the field, experience would take over in making these critical judgment calls by the wave of a hand.

Billing the Customer

Before accepting to do a job or begin to do a job, ensure there is a job order. Part of your initial discussions with the client helps you to mentally estimate all the possible costs based on;

- The probability of parts change and replacement parts' cost.
- Your established standard service fee for any hardware repair.
- Your established standard service fee for any software repair.
- A combination of any one, two or three of the above.

By all means avoid overpricing or ripping off your customers. Learn to give more value than is being paid for in cash by each customer. Strike a balance between overpricing and underpricing your services. It is never good to demand additional pay after an initial agreement. Be consistent with your standards and focus on the quality of your service, in this way you will gain the customers' trust and make your business successful.

Time Management

One of the killers of successful MPSCs is the inability to space out their service delivery time for each job order and meeting deadlines for collection even while successful with the repair jobs. You must estimate accurately what time it will take to satisfy each customer.

While it is a first-come-first-serve system at the job order collection time, it is not the same with job order completion time as it is based on;

- Which job requires the least effort, time and money for replacement parts;
- Which job brings in the fastest income and probably the fattest completion time too;
- What job takes up valuable time, which requires study and probably research at a later non-rush hour!

One of the worst case scenario that can also undermine an MPSC's competence value and drive traffic away quickly on a work day is when customers converge for collection almost at the same time or period of time, one after the other with first time customers present and the technician or his reception staff are mostly returning unrepaired customers' devices. Wrong timing! It is like visiting a clinic or hospital where a lot of dead patients are being recorded at an alarming rate. You will surely check out, citing any kind of excuse.

Timing is very important here, and managed with wisdom too. Even if it so happens that those who converged at such a time you are about engaging new clients are those whose devices failed repairs for genuine reasons on your part, having done your utmost best, do any of the following;

- Have them wait out the time you are engaging new clients to clear your reception area. Bad news is bad market!
- If all persons present are for collection of their devices, should you have to announce one bad news, be sure there are two other successful ones to accentuate your competence; by the way, start with the successfully completed jobs!
- When there are more failed jobs than successful ones, rather than make such announcements, choose to delay their collection than allow three or four disappointed, disgruntled and dissatisfied people show there exasperation around your premises in unison. It is negative publicity to your brand. However, the sweetest moment is when discharging multiple successful jobs simultaneously – they will all be singing the praise of that service center and that, is positive PR.

Whereas producing excellence is the ultimate goal of this book, these scenarios do play out in reality at some time or another. Some received jobs are already dead on arrival, sometimes due to the actions of the owner or some other MPSCs. That, cannot be your fault and should not be allowed to rub your business wrongly when competence is actually in place. Be wise!

Most importantly, do not allow the impatience of some clients to force you to undermine your reputation by returning failed jobs frequently. Calmly explain and educate them especially asking for additional time to fix their device.

Your competence, matched with technical acuity and intuition should be applied on very challenging situations that would require your keen application of delay. Delay the discharge of that device until your perseverance pays off.

Your primary duty is to deliver on the job and that, will help you build a powerful reputation quickly. If you lose that job to another MPSC that delivers successful repairs, imagine what damage to your competence and hence, patronage. Word of mouth de-marketing is powerfully destructive.

Dealing with Difficult Clients

In every business, there are usually bound to be troublesome situations. How you handle such situations will make or mar your business whether you are in the right or wrong side. What to do?

- ✓ Recognize troublesome personalities on time and follow duly established processes and standard business procedures. Usually they are the ones seeking a relaxation of such standards at collection point. It is stated earlier but to state it again, do not relax it for anyone.
- ✓ If an issue of dispute yet arises, focus on the damage the effect is having or going to have on your business and brand should it be allowed to linger. Hence find a quick compromise and discharge such a person quickly even if at a financial loss, otherwise use the full weight of the law.
- ✓ By all means avoid troublesome clients. Yes you can – and do not be the problem yourself by doing the right, sensible, fair, honest, just, effective and efficient job always.

General Service Centre Operational Routines

An MPSC should basically be run on the following service routines that would help make her service delivery easy and profitable. A start-up may not have all that is required for standard operations but can grow from stage to stage, level to level, with time. It is possible to pick out those that are within reach for any service capacity level or stage.

They include;

- Register and document jobs and maintain records which include a database of your client list with contact information. This is helpful for targeted marketing and numerous opportunities in future. Note their device status after repairs to identify those among your positive PR leads.

- Stock replacement parts. This eases your operations and operational cost. If finance is yet a challenge, establish a relationship with one or two sources that deliver your needs efficiently.
- As you grow, employ and train your front office support staff effectively as that is where the money is made – at collection point; and that is where money and patronage is lost too!
- Keep your computer system hooked to the internet and support forums like GSM forum by ZFrank.

Think Numbers!

Finally in concluding this book, I want to encourage you as an entrepreneur to think in terms of numbers. How much of your product or service that can reach the highest number of the population is the key to success.

Here is wishing you success ahead.

Shalom!

To God Be the Glory.

Notes

[1]. Hill, Napoleon "Specialized Knowledge Personal Experiences or Observations" (chapter 5), Think and Grow Rich (1960 revised edition), Fawcett books, New York.
[2]. Ibid.

[3]. "Communication". Wikipedia
(https://en.wikipedia.org/wiki/Communication), Accessed 28 October 2015

[4]. http://www.dictionary.com/browse/mobile

[5]. "GSM" (2015). Wikipedia, (https://en.wikipedia.org/wiki/GSM), Accessed 27th October 2015.

[6]. "1G". Wikipedia (https://en.wikipedia.org/wiki/1G), Accessed 27th October 2015.

[7]. 3rd Generation Partnership Project (June 2015). "3GGP TS45.001: Technical Specification Group GSM/EDGE Radio Access Network; Mobile Station (MS) - Base Station System (BSS) interface; Radio Link Control / Medium Access Control (RLC/MAC) protocol; section 10.0a.1 - GPRS RLC/MAC block for data transfer". 12.5.0. Retrieved 2015-12-05

[8]. Welt. H. Anatomy of contemporary GSM cellphone hardware, April 2010, http://laforge.gnumonks.org/papers/gsm_phone-anatomy-latest.pdf Accessed on 11 January 2015.

[9]. Baseband processor (2015),
http://en.wikipedia.org/wiki/Baseband_processor Accessed on 14th July 2015.

[10]. "RAM". Wikipedia,
(https://en.wikipedia.org/wiki/Random-access_memory)

[11]. Ibid.

[12]. "Flash Memory". Wikipedia
(https://en.wikipedia.org/wiki/Random-access_memory)

[13]. ibid.

[14]. "Integrated circuits". Wikipedia,
(https://en.wikipedia.org/wiki/Integrated_circuit)

[15]. ibid.

[16]. ibid.

[17]. Rouse, Margaret (March 27, 2007). **"Definition: multi-core processor"**. TechTarget. Archived from **the original** on August 5, 2010. Retrieved March 6, 2013.

Buy the first edition at Amazon. It will help build your foundations in electronic repairs, in addition to this updated Second Edition.

Mobile Phones and Tablets Repairs: A Complete Guide for Beginners and Professionals 1st Edition

by Chukky Oparandu ˅ (Author)

⭐⭐⭐⭐☆ ˅   50 ratings

> See all formats and editions

Kindle	Paperback
$9.99	**$25.50**
Read with Our **Free App**	2 Used from $31.65
	5 New from $25.73

Look inside ↓

IT Career: A Road Map 1st Edition

by Chukky Oparandu ˅ (Author)

⭐⭐⭐⭐☆ ˅   2 ratings

> See all formats and editions

Kindle	Paperback
$7.50	**$9.99**
Read with Our **Free App**	1 Used from $13.62
	4 New from $9.99

The book "IT Career: A Roadmap" is designed to provide guidance, clarify confusions and enumerate recommended pathways into the information technology industry for various categories of interests such as aspiring high school leavers, undergraduate students, graduate students, professionals in IT or other sectors who wish to IT-enable their careers as well as job seekers.

About The Author

Chukky Oparandu is the author these two books;

a. Mobile Phones and Tablets Repairs: A Complete Guide for Beginners and Professionals, © 2016
b. IT Career: A Roadmap, © 2017

He holds a Master of Science degree (MSc.) in Information Technology, Bachelor of Engineering in Electrical/Computer Engineering and a National Diploma in Electrical/Electronic Engineering. He also holds multiple industry standard certifications from major OEMs like Cisco Systems and Oracle. He consults in Information and Communication Technology, a training consultant who has mentored a good number of individuals who run successful businesses.

Chukky personally teaches seminars nationwide in Nigeria and other African countries covering Mobile Phone Repairs, PC/ Laptop Hardware and Software (including troubleshooting, maintenance, repairs, and upgrade) and majorly, Internetworking. His classes are never boring as he has a knack for making complex topics both understandable and entertaining. If you have 10 or more people to train, Chukky can design and present a custom seminar for you or your organization's needs.

Contact Chukky by sending email to: mondraim@gmail.com

Made in the USA
Las Vegas, NV
29 October 2023

79927723R00162